CONSTANTINE

THE HELLBLAZER COLLECTION

Karen Berger	VP-Executive Editor & Editor-original series
Jonathan Vankin	Editors-original series
Stuart Moore	
Art Young	Associate Editor-original series
Pornsak Pichetshote	Assistant Editor-original series
Scott Nybakken	Editor-collected edition
Robbin Brosterman	Senior Art Director
Amie Brockway-Metcalf	Art Director
Paul Levitz	President & Publisher
Georg Brewer	VP-Design & Retail Product Development
Richard Bruning	Senior VP-Creative Director
Patrick Caldon	Senior VP-Finance & Operations
Chris Caramalis	VP-Finance
Terri Cunningham	VP-Managing Editor
Alison Gill	VP-Manufacturing
Rich Johnson	VP-Book Trade Sales
Hank Kanalz	VP-General Manager-WildStorm
Lillian Laserson	Senior VP & General Counsel
Jim Lee	Editorial Director-WildStorm
David McKillips	VP-Advertising & Custom Publishing
John Nee	VP-Business Development
Gregory Noveck	Senior VP-Creative Affairs
Cheryl Rubin	Senior VP-Brand Management
Bob Wayne	VP-Sales & Marketing

CONSTANTINE: THE HELLBLAZER COLLECTION

TABLE OF CONTENTS

Straight to Hell:
An Introduction to
John Constantine 4

Constantine: The Official Movie
Adaptation 8

Hunger 73
From HELLBLAZER #1

Hold Me 115
From HELLBLAZER #27

The Beginning of the End 141
From HELLBLAZER #41

BY MICHAEL BONNER

A TRUE STORY: In 1986, the English comics writer Alan Moore sat down at a table in a small café in Westminster, London, just a short walk from the Houses of Parliament and Big Ben. As he tucked into a round of sandwiches in this unremarkable London café, Moore looked up to see a man in a suit and rumpled trench coat walk in through the door. The man winked conspiratorially at Moore, smiled, then disappeared into another part of the café. It was an instance of fiction intruding on the real world, of fantasy made flesh — and Moore was left reeling from the experience. He'd just been "Constantined."

At that point in his career, Moore had cemented his status as one of the pre-eminent comics writers with his work on a number of highly acclaimed series, including SAGA OF THE SWAMP THING, his revisionist reworking of Len Wein and Berni Wrightson's horror title for DC Comics. A vast, lyrical and imaginative series that chronicled the extraordinary adventures of an earth elemental born from the death of doctor Alec Holland in the swamps of Louisiana, SWAMP THING addressed complex themes with a fierce intelligence that stood in sharp contrast to the traditional super-hero fare characteristic of the time.

One of Moore's many memorable creations in the pages of SWAMP THING was a Machiavellian, chain-smoking magician from England called John Constantine, whose dramatic debut in S.O.T.S.T. #37, in June 1985, heralded the start of Moore's ambitious "American Gothic" storyline. Moore created Constantine at the behest of his collaborators on S.O.T.S.T., artists John Totleben and Steve Bissette. Both fans of the British New Wave band The Police, they wanted to draw a character who looked like the group's bassist and vocalist, Sting, and Moore rose to the challenge.

As Moore told *Wizard* magazine in November, 1993, "I have an idea that most of the mystics in comics are generally older people, very austere, very proper, very middle class in a lot of ways. They are not at all functional on the street.

It struck me that it might be interesting for once to do an almost blue-collar warlock. Somebody who was streetwise, working class, and from a different background than the standard run of comic book mystics. Constantine started to grow out of that."

By 1986, within a year of his first appearance, this sly, sinister yet deeply charismatic figure with an alluringly mysterious past had developed from a simple extra into a notable character in his own right. As Neil Gaiman, who would occasionally write Constantine over the years, recalls, "I remember asking Alan the first time I met him whether Constantine would survive till the end of 'American Gothic.' He seemed too cool a character to kill."

1986 was a watershed year for the comics industry. The popularity of WATCHMEN, Moore's sweeping reinvention of the super-hero genre, THE DARK KNIGHT RETURNS, Frank Miller's ultra-violent take on the Batman myth, and *Maus*, Art Spiegelman's Pulitzer Prize-winning tale of survivors from Hitler's concentration camps, all alerted publishers to the potential for similar "adult" comics. This was not lost on SWAMP THING editor Karen Berger, who began to examine the possibilities of originating more comic books along comparable lines. Although she claims there was "no great defining moment when we decided to do a

> "I always think it's kind of funny that Constantine purports to be some kind of socialist/left winger in his politics, when his actual personal politics are those of the addict: ruthless, willing to sacrifice whoever and whatever it takes to get what he needs."
>
> — GARTH ENNIS

Constantine book," Berger suspected early on that Constantine had enough appeal to carry his own title. Berger relates, "He had real stage presence and an aura of mystery around him, and we felt we could expand upon, but not give away, the story of this guy."

The writer to whom this task fell was another Briton — Jamie Delano. Delano had come to comics in 1984, writing *Captain Britain* and contributing stories to *Doctor Who Monthly,* both for Marvel UK. Along with artist John Ridgway, Delano laid the foundations for Constantine which remain in place to this day, transforming a supporting character into the full-fledged star capable of carrying his own series. Delano created a world and a life beyond the Louisiana bayou for Constantine: he elaborated on his origins, identifying his place of birth as Liverpool, he gave him a family — sister Cheryl, niece Gemma, father Thomas — and established his base of operations as London, Constantine's adopted home.

"I just sit down and start the characters walking and talking in my head and hope I write down the entertaining bits," says Delano. "It's always a tricky strategy, and for a first major series, probably particularly foolhardy. With any other character I would probably have fallen flat on my face and been trampled into oblivion by the press of cooler-headed talents behind me, but Constantine seemed to come naturally."

Says Berger, "We took the approach, as we do for all of our books, that the writer really has to understand the character. If half of what the writer develops on the character never sees print, the character still has to have a history — it should be fully realized." HELLBLAZER made its debut with a January 1988 cover date (Clive Barker had already nabbed their intended title for the series, Hellraiser). Delano's two-part opening story drew the reader into John's sallow, poisonous world, as Constantine set out to defeat a hunger demon roaming New York due to the folly of an old friend, Gary Lester. Delano immediately established some of the series' prime attributes and characters: the introduction of Chas, the first appearance of the ghosts of John's dead friends, and through the eventual fate of Lester, Constantine's worrying habit of sacrificing his friends for the cause. The dramatic impact of these would be felt over time, but for now — along with the Satchmo Hawkins column Delano penned for the first two issues — they offered tantalizing insights into John's character and past.

Over the first year, Delano outlined John's family and personal history in more detail. Readers met his sister and niece, Cheryl and Gemma, when they were imperiled by the Damnation Army, and finally learned the true horror of the events at Newcastle, alluded to since Constantine's earliest appearances in SWAMP THING. In issue #11, aptly titled "Newcastle: A Taste of Things to Come," Delano flashed back to 1978, when Constantine condemned a nine-year-old girl to Hell through his own reckless-ness and inexperience. The story high-lighted the tragedy in his past, rein-forced him as a flawed anti-hero, and gave him a new depth.

"But even if it hadn't been Newcastle," says Gaiman, "he would have done something like Newcastle, because that's the kind of person he is. He's John Constantine, after all."

The story raised pointed questions, notably: why does Constantine return to magic, despite the harm it causes? Delano answers: "Because the world is fucking boring, remorse-less and inevitable. Because he's a junkie, and no price is too much to pay when you need to feel that rush of possibility scream through your veins. Because he's scared of dying."

Driven by his interests in "politics, the human condition and the 'magic' inherent in the subconscious mind," Delano refused to just sit back and simply tell horror stories. He wrote scathing satire, metaphysical fever dreams and domestic dramas, and with equal vigor tackled racism, Vietnam, government conspiracies and environmental politics. Along the way, Delano returned more frequently to Constantine's for-mative years, using the past to explore Constantine's motives and behavior even further.

"I like 'Dead Boy's Heart' (HLB #35) and 'In Another Part of Hell' (HLB #84)," says Delano, "particularly because both those stories seem to offer us glimpses of a younger, more vulnerable John Constantine, in contrast to the 'veiled complexity' which confuses our percep-tions of the older man."

Berger agrees. "For a character who has this mysterious, enigmatic aura, it's pretty rewarding when you can peek behind the curtain. I still feel there's a lot about

Constantine that I don't know, but I don't think he'd be as strong a character if we didn't know some of the details of his past."

Delano's final story was "The Magus" (HLB #40), a climactic, metaphysical journey inside Constantine, where he finally met his twin and the two became integrated. It signaled the end of the defining run on the series, though Delano would write Constantine again, unable to get the bastard off his back. Delano concludes, "John is a man constantly driven to live up to his expectations, at the same time under-mined by the knowledge that failure is inevitable and laughing himself shitless at the ridiculous spectacle of his struggle."

Delano's successor on the series was Belfast-born writer Garth Ennis, then a virtual unknown outside the UK, where he had written for *2000AD* and its short-lived sister publication, *Crisis*. It was one series for *Crisis*, called "True Faith," which caught the attention of HELLBLAZER's departing editor, Berger.

"I liked the fact that Garth dealt with such a controversial subject in such a human way," she says. "Garth is a very effective writer in terms of character portrayal, the ease with which he writes people. He's got a great ear for dialogue, and an ability to write people, to make them sound like someone that you know."

"I liked the 'ordinary bloke' aspect of Constantine," admits Ennis. "With HELLBLAZER, I could write a monthly comic fea-turing a normal, non-super-pow-ered or costumed character who moved in a recognizable world, with realistic motivation and moral behavior. His reactions would be those of a mor-tal, vulnerable man — and the fact that he was a bit of a bastard helped."

For his dramatic, six-part debut storyline, "Dangerous Habits" (HLB #41-#46) in 1991, Ennis reinforced Constantine's mortality by giving him terminal lung cancer. It was a long way from the psychological horrors Delano had visited upon Constantine, and the raw intensity and considerable humanity displayed in the story became the chief characteristics of Ennis's run.

"Dangerous Habits" also introduced

two pivotal characters to Constantine's world: the First of the Fallen and Kit Ryan.

"With the First, I wanted to give Constantine an unbeatable, terrifying adversary that would mean certain doom to him, and to create an archvillain of irredeemable, absolute bastardy," notes Ennis. "None of that he's-not-all-bad crap here, thank you."

If the First was Constantine's ultimate enemy, Kit was his true love. "Kit was supposed to be the one woman who could see through Constantine," says Ennis. "She would take none of his shit and put up with none of the danger he foists on those closest to him. Having seen him at his weakest and most vulnerable, his usual 'act' would be laughable to her."

Ennis brought a distinctive, earthy voice to HELLBLAZER. He gave John an active social life, upping Chas's role in the series from mere gopher to regular drinking partner and occasional sidekick, while much of John's relationship with Kit took place either in bed or down the pub. This added a new dimension to Constantine, giving him a more personable, down-to-earth demeanor as he swore, drank and laughed the time away with his mates. A rake at the gates of Hell, indeed.

Ennis led the reader deep into Constantine's life, though, pulling him from one emotional extreme to the other in his relationship with Kit, which remains one of the series' all-time highlights. John loved Kit, but his inability to keep the one promise he made to her — to leave her out of his magic — doomed their relationship.

Devastated, Constantine slid into self-pity and alcoholism. He lived rough on the streets of London, begging for money and food — a pitiful shadow of his former self. This was Constantine as he'd never been seen before: stripped of his charm and magic, a tragic, broken man. If the readers felt any pangs of sympathy for him after Kit's departure, they were swiftly reminded exactly what a manipulative bastard Constantine is as he prepared for his final showdown with the Devil. One by one, Constantine pulled in all the favors he was owed, cruelly exploiting friends and contacts to ensure his own survival — at whatever the cost.

"He's a junkie for magic," says Ennis. "I always think it's kind of funny that Constantine purports to be some kind of socialist/left winger in his politics, when

> "I remember asking Alan the first time I met him whether Constantine would survive till the end of 'American Gothic.' He seemed too cool a character to kill."
> — NEIL GAIMAN

his actual personal politics are those of the addict: ruthless, willing to sacrifice whoever and whatever it takes to get what he needs. He pays lip service to the idea of regretting the human cost of his dabbling, but that wears thinner and thinner as he heads for 50."

By the end of Ennis's run, the streets of London were awash with the blood of John's fallen comrades. It was the ultimate price they paid for knowing John Constantine.

Ennis's formal successor was another British writer, Paul Jenkins, who took over the title in 1995 and put yet another unique spin on the character. Jenkins, who had previously worked as an editor on titles like Dave McKean's *Cages* and Moore's *Big Numbers,* made the move to writing with the encouragement of then-HELLBLAZER editor, the late Lou Stathis. In his first major storyline, "Critical Mass" (HLB #92-#96), Jenkins resolved a number of loose ends — in particular the fates of the First of the Fallen and Astra, the young girl Constantine had sent to Hell all those years ago in Newcastle — which signified the direction he wanted the series to take.

"One loose end I felt needed resolving was Constantine's alcoholism. One minute he's got a serious drink problem, then suddenly he's a casual drinker, which in my experience doesn't happen very often," says Jenkins. "So with 'Critical Mass' I said to the reader 'Look, here's all the things Constantine's been, here's who he is and where he is,' and through a contrivance of the story I took all the bits of

Constantine I wasn't interested in, shoved them in a homunculus and sent that off to Hell, leaving me with the bits of Constantine I wanted to write about."

Significantly, Jenkins had Constantine confront his past. In a powerful 100th issue, Constantine was taken to Hell by the Devil for a reunion with his dead father. Constantine learned that his father had forced his mother to have an abortion when she was pregnant with John, the shock of which killed her. It was a horrifying revelation, shedding new light on John's already troubled relationship with his father: Constantine hadn't been wanted, he hadn't even been loved. It's no wonder he'd been drawn to magic and the escape it offered from the real world.

Jenkins continued to develop his version of Constantine. With his bad half in Hell, Constantine seemed to mellow and assume a new sense of responsibility. "Constantine is a great person," says Jenkins. "He won't suffer fools gladly, he won't be shat on. He doesn't care if it's the ultimate fascist like the First of the Fallen or some other little fascist who wants to kick some ghost out of a house, he rails against them equally. He tries to pretend that he's a mean, heartless bastard, but the way I saw it was that nobody's just one color, there has to be another side to him."

Subsequently, this new-look Constantine embarked on his first serious relationship since Kit, with an American journalist, Dani Wright. He became socially active again, mixing with old friends from his punk days, memorably Rich Eldridge (based on Jenkins's own brother), his girlfriend Michelle and their son, Syder. Indeed, Jenkins's own concerns emerged as Constantine's friendship with Rich & Co. grew. Like a lot of old punks, Rich had become involved with crusty techno travelers, champions of Green politics and primary targets of the British government's Criminal Justice Bill. Jenkins dovetailed these issues of personal liberty and environmentalism into an exploration of English myth, with Constantine visiting lost magical kingdoms and meeting legendary figures like King Arthur and Merlin.

"When I was growing up in Dorset, my family lived on a Roman road, and about half a mile away from our house was an ancient burial site," reveals Jenkins. "My

um used to say things like 'If you listen
to it at midnight, you can hear the fairies
playing,' and I used to go into the woods
at night with the guy who I wrote into
HELLBLAZER as Tom, the Jesus figure,
and feed badgers. So I saw magic every
day as a child, I became accustomed to it
as part of the land."

With Jenkins's final story arc, "How To
Play With Fire" (HLB #125-#128),
Constantine's transformation was com-
plete. For once, there were no scenes of
terrible bloodshed; Constantine's friends
walked safely away. John had sold his
soul to ensure their safety. Jenkins proved
there was another side to John, one capable
of compassion — and making the ultimate
sacrifice himself.

After Jenkins, Ennis returned briefly to
the title for "Son of Man" (HLB #129-
133), a five-part story which delved even
deeper into Constantine's relationship
with the beleaguered Chas. Following
Ennis came British scribe Warren Ellis,
who had been writing the cult hit TRANS-
METROPOLITAN for Vertigo. As with his
predecessors, Ellis brought out a different
side in the magician — one darker, more
cruel and sinister.

"Warren went back and made the book
a real, true horror title, whereas I think
Paul's run had got more into the magical
aspect of Constantine," says Berger.
"Warren grounded him again in London,
sent him back to the dark, filthy world
where Jamie had put him at the start of
the book, and pitted him against, in most
cases, a singular adversary. He narrowed
the focus a little bit more, brought
Constantine back to a microcosm."

During Ellis's run he focused on a sym-
biotic relationship between Constantine
and London, drawing on the city's grim
and lengthy magical past for inspiration.

"London and magic, for me, are all tan-
gled up together: both have undeniable
glamour, both can kick free a sense of
wonder, and both can very easily be ugly
and pretty fucking stupid-looking,"
explains Ellis. "It amused me to take a
walk round it all, from the sad bastards to
the genuinely scary people, from a pretty
face in Soho to a dead body in Spitalfields.
And speaking of dead bodies, there's a
certain strain of British crime fiction that's
not been seen in American comics, a kind
of murder writing that's blacker and sad-
der than [James] Ellroy. Derek Raymond's

'Factory' novels are the obvious touch-
stone, brutal things without a chink of
light in them. A very English kind of urban
fiction, a perfect fit with John
Constantine's world of shabby magic."

Ellis immersed Constantine in
London's secret history — from ritualistic
murder to unsettling revelations concern-
ing the origins of the British monarchy.
The old bastard, it seemed, had come
home. However, Ellis left the series pre-
maturely after only ten issues with issue
#143, after encountering problems with a
controversial story that dealt with children
and gun violence, a topic that cut too
close to home in the aftermath of the
Columbine shootings.

Following in Ellis's footsteps was the
series' first American writer, Brian
Azzarello, who brought to HELLBLAZER
the same hard-boiled intensity that char-
acterizes his other ongoing Vertigo series,
100 BULLETS. Electing to remove
Constantine from his natural environment,
Azzarello's initial story arc, "Hard Time"
(HLB #146-#150), found John sentenced
to 35 years in a maximum-security prison
somewhere in America. Playing one side
against another with consummate skill,
the slippery Constantine swiftly engi-
neered his freedom, before setting off on
a road trip around the States — with
customarily unpleasant results.

"John's a spiritual grifter, a con man
working a psychological shell game,"
proposes Azzarello. "You may be certain
where that pea is, but the only certainty is
you know where it is if he lets you. It's
this control — or illusion of control —
that lies at the heart of the character.
He may not be one step ahead of the
game, but he makes you think he is."

"Brian made John more of a manipulator again, back to the twinkle in the
eye, the more unpredictable nature,"
says Berger. "He's not as dark as,
say, during Warren's run. He's
cheekier, but still very much the
bastard. Brian's take is definitely
closer to Alan [Moore]'s vision of
the character."

During Azzarello's controversial stint on HELLBLAZER,
Constantine had managed
to travel across America,
encountering urban leg-
ends, Neo-Nazi militias and
underground sex clubs along

the way. However, when the book was
handed back to another English writer —
namely its current scribe, Mike Carey —
Constantine found himself back home in
Liverpool, reuniting with his family,
friends and old haunts. Still, wherever
Constantine goes, trouble always follows,
and under Carey's run John has had to
save his niece Gemma from an evil sor-
cerer in "Red Sepulchre" (HLB #177-
#180), thwart Armageddon in "Staring at
the Wall" (HLB #189-#193), and try to
defeat three of his "children" sired with a
dubious shape-shifting demon in "Happy
Families" (HLB #200).

With over 200 issues under his belt,
Constantine still manages to maintain his
status as one of the most complex and
fascinating characters in comics — a man
with a tragic, blood-soaked past, whose
behavior is ambiguous at the best of
times and terrifying at the worst. He's one
of the truly great anti-heroes comics will
ever know. "Flawed, smart, funny and
cool," says Gaiman. "He's also a dick-
headed, stubborn idiot, who causes nothing but doom and misery for his loved
ones and friends."

"[We all] have the secret desire to walk
the walk, fuck with the immensely powerful and not worry about any comeback,
and never be stuck for a line," adds Garth
Ennis on John's continued popularity.
"And girls. They fancy him." •

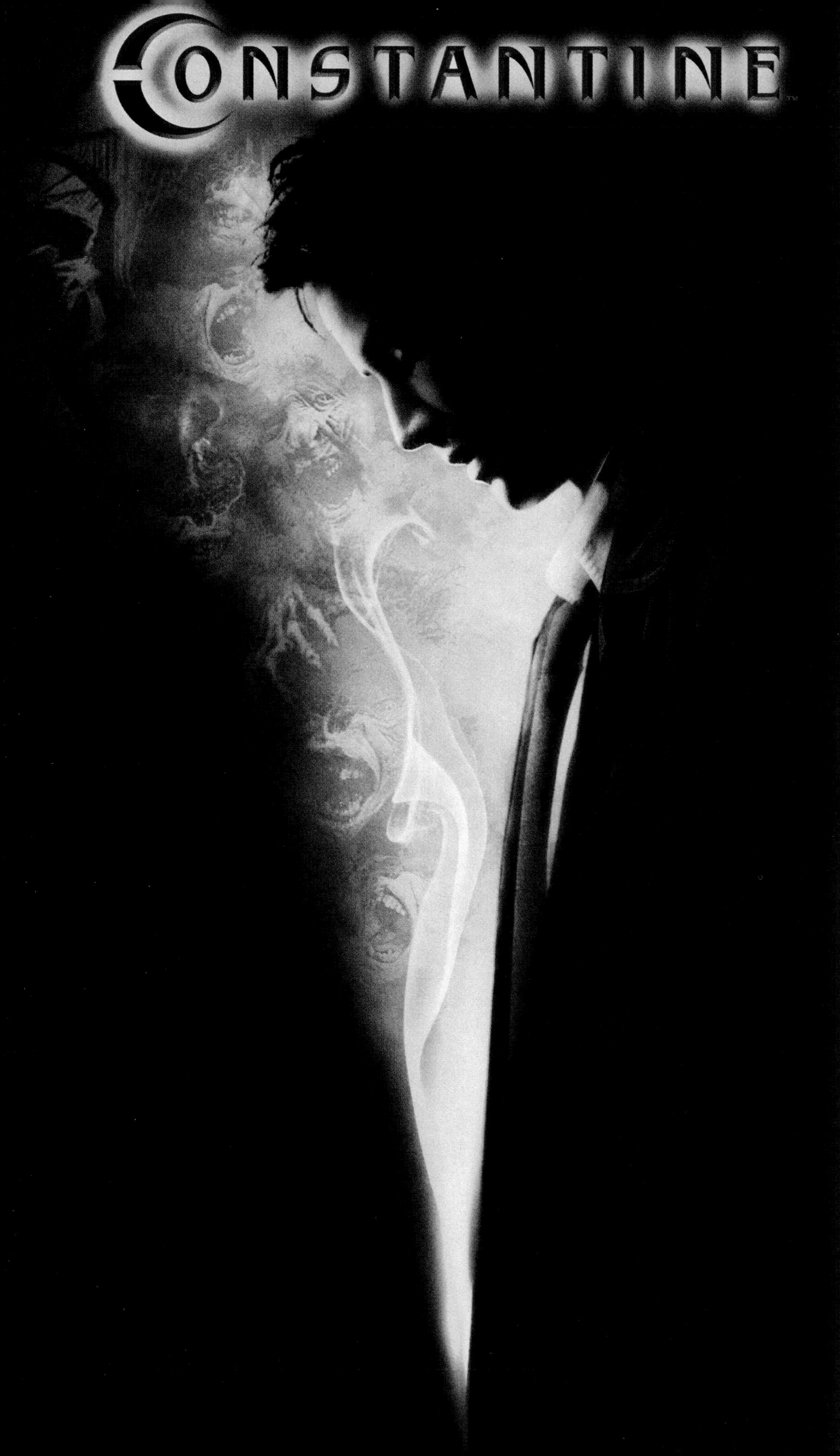
CONSTANTINE™

CONSTANTINE
THE MOVIE

Steven T. Seagle
WRITER

Ron Randall
PENCILLER

Jimmy Palmiotti
INKER

Peter Gross
BREAKDOWNS

Lee Loughridge
COLORIST

Jared K. Fletcher
LETTERER

WHAT THE HELL IS GOING ON HERE?

WE CAN'T STAY IN THERE, DETECTIVE WEISS-- IT'S-- IT'S HELL.

WHAT IS IT?

YOU HEARD HIM, IT'S *HELL.*

YOU? WHAT'RE YOU DOING HERE?

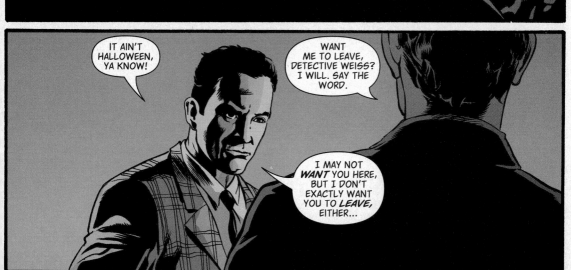

IT AIN'T *WANT* HALLOWEEN, YA KNOW!

WANT ME TO LEAVE, DETECTIVE WEISS? I WILL. SAY THE WORD.

I MAY NOT *WANT* YOU HERE, BUT I DON'T EXACTLY WANT YOU TO *LEAVE,* EITHER...

JOHN! THANK GOD YOU CAME! I THINK-- I FOUND YOU ONE.

LOOK, I *CALLED* YOU, RIGHT?

I TRIED TO PULL IT OUT *MYSELF*, BUT I, I--

NOT EASY TO PERFORM AN EXORCISM WHEN YOU'RE *DRUNK*, IS IT?

I KNEW YOU COULDN'T STAY ON THE WAGON.

YOU WANT TO BE USEFUL, FATHER?

TELL THE COPS TO BRING ME A *MIRROR*.

A *BIG* MIRROR.

STONE FRAGMENTS FROM THE ROAD TO DAMASCUS... BULLET SHAVINGS FROM THE ASSASSINATION ATTEMPT ON THE POPE...

THIS IS GOOD! PIECE OF THE *SHROUD* MOSES WORE TO THE *MOUNTAIN.* VERY, VERY *FLAMMABLE.*

AND YOU'LL LOVE THIS... *SCREECH* BEETLE FROM *AMITYVILLE....*

TO YOU AND ME, IT'S NOTHING. BUT TO THE *FALLEN,* IT'S LIKE NAILS ON CHALKBOARDS.

OK, FINE. YOU WANT THE HIGH QUALITY STUFF--

I GOT IT. I KNOW A GUY KNOWS A GUY AND--

GOLD WAS BLESSED BY THE BISHOP ANICOTT DURING THE CRUSADES.

ANYONE SAYS IT'S A SOFT METAL NEVER GOT PUNCHED IN THE CHOPS WITH *THESE* BEAUTIES!

SO, UH, WHAT'S THE ACTION, ANYWAY? WHY YOU NEED THE STUFF?

SOLDIER DEMON IN A LITTLE GIRL...

...IT WAS TRYING TO COME *THROUGH...*

JESUS...

MORNING.

SURE YOU'RE *READY* FOR THIS, ANGIE?

DO IT.

NO...!

...ISABEL? NO! *NO!*

SHE-- SHE *FELL* FROM THE ROOF? HOW COULD SHE--

JUMPED. SHE JUMPED FROM THE ROOF, ANGIE. YOU NEVER TOLD US YOU HAD A TWIN SIS--

ISABEL WOULDN'T KILL HERSELF!

ANGIE...

SHE *WOULDN'T,* WEISS!

DETECTIVE. THERE WAS *SURVEILLANCE.* LOOK AT THE *FILM.* SEE FOR YOURSELF...

YOU CAN SEE IT RIGHT HERE.

LUNG CANCER.

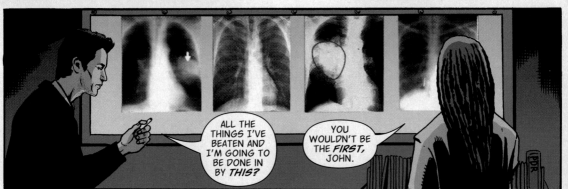

ALL THE THINGS I'VE BEATEN AND I'M GOING TO BE DONE IN BY *THIS?*

YOU WOULDN'T BE THE *FIRST,* JOHN.

I'VE DEFEATED THINGS PEOPLE HAVE NEVER EVEN *HEARD* OF.

C'MON, YOU SAVED ME BEFORE. YOU CAN DO IT *AGAIN,* RIGHT?

THIS IS... AGGRESSIVE.

YOU... YOU REALLY NEED TO PREPARE... MAKE ARRANGEMENTS.

NO NEED.

I KNOW EXACTLY WHERE I'M GOING...

St. Anthony's Theological Society.

SHE **HAS** TO HAVE A CATHOLIC FUNERAL, FATHER. SHE HAS TO!

IT IS A MORTAL SIN TO--

--DAVID... THIS IS *ISABEL* WE'RE TALKING ABOUT.

SHE DID **NOT** COMMIT SUICIDE!

THE BISHOP BELIEVES *OTHERWISE.* YOU KNOW THE *RULES,* ANGELA!

RULES? *PLEASE.*

GOING DOWN?

NOT IF I CAN *HELP* IT.

I KNOW WHAT YOU **WANT**, SON...

STILL KEEPING YOUR ALL-SEEING EYE ON ME, **GABRIEL**?

I WOULD SAY A SHEPHERD LEADS EVEN THE MOST WAY-WARD OF HIS FLOCK, BUT IT MIGHT SOUND **DISINGENUOUS**.

BESIDES, YOU'VE WASTED **YOUR** CHANCE AT REDEMPTION, JOHN. YOU'RE **NOT** GOING TO THE **FAIR**.

WHAT ABOUT THE MINIONS I'VE SENT **BACK** TO HELL?

HAVEN'T I SERVED HIM **ENOUGH**? WHAT DOES HE **WANT** FROM ME?

THE **USUAL**. SELF-SACRIFICE. **BELIEF**.

ENTRY INTO HEAVEN REQUIRES **FAITH**. BELIEF **WITHOUT** PROOF. YOU'VE SEEN--

I NEVER **ASKED** TO SEE, I WAS **BORN** WITH THIS CURSE.

GIFT. A GIFT YOU'VE **SQUANDERED**.

ALL YOU'VE EVER DONE YOU HAVE DONE FOR **YOURSELF**. DON'T COME WHIMPERING TO ME NOW BECAUSE YOU'RE GOING TO HELL.

YOU'RE GOING TO DIE BECAUSE YOU SMOKED 30 CIGARETTES A DAY SINCE YOU WERE FIFTEEN.

AND YOU'RE GOING TO **HELL** BECAUSE YOU TOOK A **LIFE**. TO PUT IT IN A WAY YOUR KIND WOULD **UNDERSTAND**...

YOU'RE **FUCKED**.

CONSTANTINE! OVER *HERE*, JOHN! HURRY UP!

"THERE WAS *SURVEILLANCE*."

"LOOK AT THE *FILM.*"

"SEE FOR YOURSELF...."

OH, ISABEL... NO...

CONSTANTINE.

"CONSTANTINE"...?

CONSTANTINE! OVER *HERE*, JOHN! HURRY UP!

CLAKTA CLIK CLIK CLAK

JOHN CONSTANTINE

SATANIC CULT MURDER:

ASSAULT ON ALLEGEDLY POSSESSED BISHOP:

LONDON WITCH COVEN REQUESTS EXTRADITION:

Insufficient

SATANIC CULT MURDER:

Insufficient evidence

ASSAULT ON ALLEGEDLY POSSESSED BISHOP:

Insufficient evidence

LONDON WITCH COVEN REQUESTS EXTRADITION:

Insufficient evidence

TWO FROGS ON A BENCH.

I'M WITH HIM.

UH... TWO FROGS ON A BENCH.

Club Tarot

I HATE THIS PLACE!

WELL, WELL, WELL, LOOK WHAT THE ANTICHRIST DRAGGED IN.

NOT NOW.

HEY, JOHNNY.

NOT NOW.

COME IN, JOHN!

MIDNITE? THIS THING'S *NEVER* GOING TO *BALANCE*, YOU KNOW.

MATERIAL

AH, BUT IT ALWAYS *DOES.*

YOU'VE BEEN *ABSENT* FOR SOME TIME. HAVE YOU COME HERE WITH *RELICS* TO SELL?

NO, I'M ≥COUGH≤ *OUT* OF THAT-- ≥COUGH≤

AH, I *SEE* NOW. YOUR *HEALTH* IS BAD. HOW LONG?

A FEW MONTHS MAYBE...

WELL, I'M CERTAIN YOU DIDN'T COME HERE FOR A SYMPATHETIC *SHOULDER* TO CRY ON.

I SAW A SOLDIER DEMON TRY TO PUNCH ITS WAY OUT THROUGH A LITTLE GIRL.

NOT A HALF-BREED. A FULL-FLEDGED *DEMON.* HERE. ON *OUR* PLANE.

CLEARLY, I DO NOT HAVE TO REMIND YOU THAT IS *IMPOSSIBLE.*

MARAUDING ARMIES OF DEMONS ARE JUST *TALES* SPUN TO SCARE SCHOOL-GIRLS.

DEMONS STAY IN *HELL,* ANGELS IN *HEAVEN*-- THE GREAT DETENTE OF THE *ORIGINAL* SUPER POWERS.

THANKS FOR THE LESSON; YOU'VE BEEN A GREAT HELP.

NOW, I NEED TO USE *THE CHAIR* TO--

JOHN... JOHN... *FORGETTING* THE FACT THAT THE CHAIR WOULD CERTAINLY *KILL* YOU...

YOU KNOW I AM *SWITZERLAND...* NEUTRAL.

HOW ELSE CAN I PROVIDE AN ESTABLISHMENT WHERE MY PATRONS CAN LET THEIR HAIR DOWN?

YOU WERE ONE WITCH DOCTOR AGAINST, WHAT, *THIRTY* ASHGAR?

AND I WAS--

YOU *WERE* CONSTANTINE. *THE* JOHN CONSTANTINE. *ONCE...*

BUT BALANCES *SHIFT.* TIMES *CHANGE.* AND I AM A *BUSINESS-MAN* FIRST. YOU *KNOW* THAT, JOHN.

THIS *ISN'T* THE USUAL GAME! SOMETHING'S *COMING!* I CAN *FEEL* IT!

OOH... *SPOOKY!*

WELCOME TO MY LIFE.

JOHN CONSTANTINE...?

WE MET, KIND OF, AT *RAVENSCAR HOSPITAL*...?

I REMEMBER.

I'D LIKE TO ASK YOU A FEW QUESTIONS, IF--

NOT REALLY IN A TALKING *MOOD*--

ALWAYS A CATCH. COME IN.

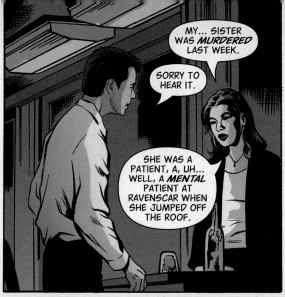

MY... SISTER WAS *MURDERED* LAST WEEK.

SORRY TO HEAR IT.

SHE WAS A PATIENT, A, UH... WELL, A *MENTAL* PATIENT AT RAVENSCAR WHEN SHE JUMPED OFF THE ROOF.

THOUGHT YOU SAID SHE WAS *MURDERED.*

ISABEL WOULD NEVER TAKE HER OWN LIFE.

SURE. WHAT KIND OF MENTAL PATIENT KILLS HERSELF? THAT WOULD BE CRAZY.

I'M NOT EVEN SURE WHY I'M *HERE,* I JUST... I'VE HEARD YOUR *NAME* FROM-- WELL... *AROUND...*

SO I READ YOUR *FILES* AT THE STATION. QUITE A MIX... OCCULT, EXORCISM, DEMONOLOGY...

BEFORE SHE WAS COMMITTED, MY SISTER WAS TALKING ABOUT *THINGS.* ANGELS...

...DEMONS. I BELIEVE SOMEONE MAY HAVE *GOTTEN* TO HER. *BRAINWASHED* HER. SOME *RELIGIOUS* CULT OR... OR SOMETHING.

SOUNDS LIKE A THEORY. GOOD LUCK ON THAT.

I THOUGHT... WITH YOUR *BACK-GROUND* YOU COULD... POINT ME IN THE RIGHT *DIRECTION?*

YEAH, OKAY. SURE...

MY SISTER WOULD NEVER KILL HERSELF. SHE WAS A *DEEPLY* DEVOUT *CATHOLIC.*

DO YOU UNDERSTAND WHAT THAT MEANS?

THAT IF SHE OFFED HERSELF, HER SOUL WOULD GO STRAIGHT TO HELL WHERE SHE'D BE RIPPED TO BLOODY CHUNKS FOR ALL ETERNITY.

THAT IT? THAT ABOUT RIGHT?

I HOPE YOU BURN THERE *WITH* HER.

BELIEVE IN SECOND CHANCES?

PRIVATE

DETECTIVE!

GO TO HELL!

YOU *CAN* *COUNT* ON IT.

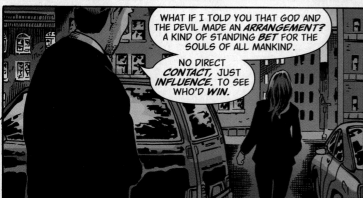

WHAT IF I TOLD YOU THAT GOD AND THE DEVIL MADE AN *ARRANGEMENT?* A KIND OF STANDING *BET* FOR THE SOULS OF ALL MANKIND.

NO DIRECT *CONTACT,* JUST *INFLUENCE.* TO SEE WHO'D *WIN.*

WHAT, SO WHEN A WOMAN'S *MURDERED* OR A MOTHER DROWNS HER *BABY,* I SHOULD GO LOOKING FOR A DEMON WITH HORNS? I DON'T *THINK* SO.

PEOPLE ARE EVIL, MR. CONSTANTINE. *PEOPLE.*

I DON'T *BELIEVE* IN THE DEVIL.

YOU *SHOULD...* HE BELIEVES IN *US.*

BLACKOUT?

NOT... LIKELY. WE SHOULD *GO...*

FAST!

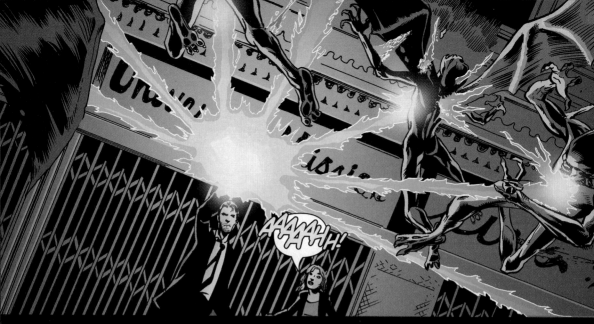

AAAAAH!

≥HUKKK!≤

DON'T WORRY, HAPPENS TO **EVERYONE** THE FIRST TIME.

IT'S THE **SULFUR**.

WHAT THE HELL **WERE** THOSE THINGS?

SEPLAVITES, ACTUALLY. SCAVENGERS FOR THE DAMNED...

...AND I DON'T THINK THEY WERE AFTER **ME**.

YOU REALLY BELIEVE YOUR SISTER WOULDN'T KILL HERSELF?

NEVER IN A MILLION YEARS.

LET'S BE **SURE**.

WHAT? HOW?

SIMPLE. SEE IF SHE'S IN HELL.

ISABEL!

CONSTANTINE...

ISABEL...

CONSTANTINE...? ARE YOU ALL RIGHT?

I... NEED TO EAT.

GRAND CENTRAL MARKET

TORTAS $5

PRODUCE

WHEN I WAS A KID, I SAW THINGS...

THINGS PEOPLE AREN'T *SUPPOSED* TO SEE.

THINGS A KID SHOULDN'T *HAVE* TO SEE.

MY PARENTS DID WHAT MOST PARENTS WOULD DO... MADE IT *WORSE.*

SHOCK TREATMENTS... *EXORCISMS...* ALL LIKE TRYING TO PULL A TOOTH THAT ISN'T THERE.

YOU TRIED TO KILL YOURSELF?

I DIDN'T *TRY* ANYTHING, ANGELA.

BUT YOU'RE STILL *HERE. ALIVE.*

NOT *MY* DOING.

OFFICIALLY, I WAS *DEAD* FOR TWO MINUTES.

HEAVEN WOULD LOOK GOOD TO YOU TOO--

IF YOU WERE A SUICIDE SENTENCED TO A PRISON WHERE HALF THE INMATES WERE *PUT* THERE BY *YOU.*

J-J-JJJ-JJ-JOHN--

--HKK!

HENNESSY? WHAT THE HELL ARE YOU DOING HE--

AHH!

THIR... STY...

WHAT... HAPPENED TO HIM...?

ALWAYS KNEW HE'D DRINK HIMSELF TO DEATH-- BUT NOT THIS QUICK.

TAKE ME TO WHERE ISABEL DIED. NOW.

RAVENSCAR PSYCHIATRIC WARD.

HER ROOM IS RIGHT--

ISABEL!

200-207 ⟶
208-215
216-224

NO, BARRY, THAT'S *NOT* ISABEL.

I'M SORRY, HE KIND OF HAD A CRUSH ON YOUR SISTER.

YOU DIDN'T TELL ME YOU WERE *TWINS*.

YOU DIDN'T ASK.

YOU KNOW, I *AM* A COP. I SEARCHED THIS ROOM. IT'S *CLEAN*.

YOU DON'T WALK OFF A BUILDING WITH-OUT LEAVING *SOMETHING* BEHIND.

I'M GUESSING... *HERE*.

"CORINTHIANS 14:01"? THERE IS NO 14TH ACT IN CORINTHIANS.

CORINTHIANS GOES *21* ACTS IN THE BOOK OF *ETHENIUS*...

...THAT'S THE BIBLE IN HELL.

44

THEY HAVE A *BIBLE* IN HELL?

YEAH, PAINTS A *DIFFERENT* VIEW OF REVELATIONS...

SAYS THE WORLD WON'T END BY *GOD'S* HAND BUT BE REBORN IN THE EMBRACE OF THE *DAMNED*.

THOUGH IF YOU ASK ME... FIRE'S FIRE.

AND THEY'RE GOING TO HAVE THIS "HELL BIBLE" HERE IN A HOSPITAL CHAPEL?

NOPE. I HAVE TO GO GET IT--

--FROM HELL.

THE SINS OF THE FATHER WILL BE EXCEEDED ONLY BY THE SINS OF THE SON...

...HIS... SON...

WHOSE SON? *GOD'S*?

NO... THE *OTHER* ONE. THE *DEVIL* HAD A SON *TOO*. MAMMON.

JOHN, IT'S BEEMAN. I WENT THROUGH SOME ANCIENT TEXTS AND I FOUND IT--

BUT, IT'S *NOT* GOOD.

AS YOU KNOW, THE MYTH SAYS MAMMON WAS CONCEIVED *BEFORE* HIS FATHER'S FALL FROM GRACE...

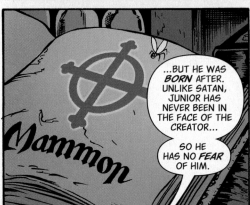

Mammon

...BUT HE WAS *BORN* AFTER. UNLIKE SATAN, JUNIOR HAS NEVER BEEN IN THE FACE OF THE CREATOR...

SO HE HAS NO *FEAR* OF HIM.

AND WHILE *DEMONS* CAN'T CROSS OVER, MAMMON WAS *CONCEIVED* IN HEAVEN, BUT *BORN* IN HELL.

THAT'S A *LOOP-HOLE. NORMAL* BARRIERS WON'T APPLY, WITH DIVINE INTERVENTION AND POSSESSION OF AN ORACLE, OR A *PSYCHIC*, HE CAN-CA-C-

HURKKTT

BEEMAN--?
HELLO...?

BEEMA--
AH--

HUKKT!
SPUTT!
PUH--!

YOU NEED A
DOCTOR.

I'VE SEEN
A DOCTOR.

IT'S YOU
I'M WORRIED
ABOUT. MAMMON
WANTED ISABEL...
AND YOU WERE
TWINS...

I'M NOT
ISABEL.

BUT YOU HAVE THE
VISION, DON'T YOU?

YOU CAN SEE
THINGS, JUST
LIKE SHE DID,
CAN'T YOU?

YES,
ALL RIGHT?
I USED TO
SEE THINGS
TOO.

BUT ONCE I SAW
THAT THEY WERE
GIVING ISABEL
PILLS FOR WHAT
SHE SAW, I
PRETENDED I DIDN'T.

BUT
I'M DONE
PRETENDING.
I WANT TO
SEE HELL.
SHOW ME
HOW.

I DON'T NEED
ANOTHER GHOST
HAUNTING ME--

SHOW ME
HOW.

AAAAHH!

...JOHN...?

BACK ALREADY? HOW WAS IT?

HORRIBLE. I-- I SAW ISABEL... GUYS I'D SHOT... SOME THING NAMED BALTHAZAR, AND I...

WHAT ARE YOU DOING?

I WAS THINKING ABOUT BALTHAZAR MYSELF. HENNESSY AND BEEMAN'S DEATHS STINK OF HIM.

LOUSY HALF-BREED STARTED KILLING MY FRIENDS TO TIP THE SCALES...

I'M ADDING SOME COUNTER-WEIGHT.

BLAM

WHAT'S GOT YOU SO JUMPY, LITTLE FRIEN--

GAAH!

BOOM

YOU *KILLED* MY FRIENDS, YOU HALF-BREED PIECE OF CRAP!

NOW IT'S *YOUR* TURN.

BUT FIRST, BALTHAZAR, TELL ME ONE THING--

HOW'S MAMMON PLANNING TO CROSS OVER?

YOU WOULDN'T *DARE* KILL ME...

YOU'RE GOING BACK TO HELL.

TRUE. BUT *YOU'RE* NOT.

NHH! WHA-- UHH!?

I'M *CLEANSING* YOU, THEN READING YOU YOUR *LAST RITES.*

YOU'RE HALF-*HUMAN*, THAT MAKES YOU ELIGIBLE TO BE *FORGIVEN.*

HSSS!

A DEMON IN HEAVEN-- LOVE TO BE A FLY ON *THAT* WALL.

"*MAY GOD HAVE MERCY ON YOUR SOUL AND GRANT YOU PARDON--*"

NOOOO!

SANGRE DE DIO! SANGRE DE DIO--!

THEN TELL ME HOW MAMMON'S PLANNING TO CROSS!

WHAT KILLED THE SON OF GOD WILL GIVE BIRTH TO THE SON OF THE DEVIL!

NOW STOP! I CAN'T GO TO HEAVEN! I *CAN'T!*

BY THE WAY, YOU HAVE TO *ASK* FOR ABSOLUTION TO BE SAVED, MORON.

BLAM

THEY TOOK *ANGELA*...

WHO DID?

DOWNTOWN.

ANGELES

SANTA MONICA

"SOMEONE WITH A NASTY PLAN IN MIND...."

BIRD ON A LADDER.

SORRY. YOU'LL HAVE TO--

GUESS AGAIN.

COOL!

HAVE YOU *LOST* WHAT LITTLE MIND YOU *HAVE?*

DON'T EVEN *THINK* ABOUT CASTING ANY *SPELLS,* MIDNITE.

I WANT THE *CHAIR.* NOW.

YOU *DARE?* IN *MY* HOUSE?!

I OFFER NO AID TO ONE SIDE OR THE OTHER. THE *BALANCE--*

YOU'RE THE *ONLY ONE* PLAYING BY THOSE *RULES,* MIDNITE!

AND WHILE YOU IMITATE SWITZERLAND, WE'RE AT *WAR.* AND *MY* FRIENDS ARE DYING! I *NEED* THE *CHAIR!*

HOW LONG'S IT BEEN SINCE YOU SURFED?

IT'S LIKE RIDING A BIKE.

NOT REALLY, NO.

WAIT, YOU'RE GOING TO *FRY* YOURSELF? DIE?

CLOSE, CHAZ. BUT NOT QUITE.

THE ELECTRIC CHAIR FROM SING SING PRISON-- OVER 200 SOULS PASSED THROUGH HERE.

NOW IT'S LIKE AN INTERNET HOOKUP FOR THE DAMNED.

I'M GOING TO SURF THE ECTO-NET.

BEFORE I DO THIS, JUST TELL ME IT *ISN'T* ABOUT THE *GIRL*.

THIS IS DEFINITELY, MOSTLY, SOMEWHAT NOT ABOUT THE GIRL.

DO IT.

SKLZZKT

GAAAAHH!

...NNNHNNHNN...

KX-1493

RAVENSCAR

...NNNGAAH!

ANY LUCK?

YEAH, FOUND THE ≥NH≤ BASTARD. BUT THE THING IS, A PLOT LIKE *THIS* TAKES *CENTURIES* OF PLANNING, SO--

SO YOU'D BETTER BE WORRIED ABOUT WHO'S *HELPING* HIM.

LET'S *GO.*

WHERE TO?

WHERE IT ALL *STARTED* IS WHERE IT'S ALL GONNA *END.*

AAAAAHH!

NNH-- *NO!* HNHH!

KFHT CU YUR YFDIN IHRYƧ!

KFHT CU YUR YFDIN IHRYƧ!

AAAAHH!

EEEEE!

HEY EVERYBODY. MY NAME'S JOHN.

COME ON NOW.

ALL TOGETHER.

HIII-III JOHN.

THIS ISN'T A MEETING? DAMN.

OKAY, THEN. YOU ARE ALL IN VIOLATION OF THE BALANCE.

LEAVE IMMEDIATELY.

AND IF WE DON'T?

FLKT

THEN GO TO HELL.

THIS IS YOUR PLAN? WATER?

YOU PRESUME TO JUDGE *ME*, JOHN?

AND THE *WICKED* SHALL INHERIT THE EARTH...

FIGURES IT WOULD BE YOU... *GABRIEL.*

NNHHH...

WHY? WHY ARE EACH OF YOU OFFERED THIS PRECIOUS GIFT OF REDEMPTION FROM THE CREATOR?

NONE IS LOVED SO, FORGIVEN SO, AS *MAN.* AND WHAT DO YOU *DO* WITH THIS GIFT?

TAKE HIS LOVE AND *SPIT* ON IT. COMMIT UPON EACH OTHER ATROCITIES OF BOTH BODY *AND* SOUL...

CONFIDENT THAT A SIMPLE "FORGIVE ME LORD" WILL GRANT YOU ACCEPTANCE UNTO HIS KINGDOM.

I HAVE WATCHED OVER THE YEARS. ONLY AS YOUR CITIES BURN DO YOU RUSH TO SAVE EACH OTHER.

ONLY IN THE FACE OF *HORROR* DO YOU FIND YOUR *NOBLER* SELVES.

SO I WILL BRING FORTH THE SON OF THE FALLEN ONE. I WILL *BRING* YOU *PAIN.* AND I WILL MAKE YOU *WORTHY* OF GOD'S LOVE.

STOP.

GO.

FAA-THER...

LUCIFER--!

THIS WORLD IS *MINE*, GABRIEL. AT LEAST IN TIME.

AIEEEEEE!

SAY GOODBYE TO THE SUN...

...BOTH OF YOU.

FATHER! NOOOOOOO!

>KOFF< J-JOHN...? >HAKK<

HNNN...

I CAN *BREATHE* AGAIN...

MY *WRISTS,* I...

YOU SAVED MY LIFE, STRANDED ME HERE ON EARTH.

GUESS YOU REALLY SHOWED *ME.*

I'LL SEE YOU *SOON,* CONSTANTINE.

NOT IF I SEE YOU *FIRST.*

FOREST LAWN CEMETERY.

REST IN PEACE.

CHAZ KRAMER

STILL FINDING HIS WAY

YA DID GOOD, KID.

READY?

AS I EVER AM.

STRANGE HOW IT ALL WORKS OUT, ISN'T IT?

MYSTERIOUS WAYS...

SOME PEOPLE LIKE IT...

SOME PEOPLE DON'T.

End

HUNGER

Jamie Delano
WRITER

John Ridgway
ARTIST

Lovern Kindzierski
COLORIST

Annie Halfacree
LETTERER

Dave McKean
COVER ARTIST

HENRY WAMBACH DOESN'T FEEL SO GOOD. SOMETHING **BLACK** AND **HUNGRY** NESTLES IN HIS GUT.

HIS HEAD BUZZES LIKE A **HIVE.**

TWENTY YEARS HE'S RUN THE **GREENWICH VILLAGE POST OFFICE,** NEVER ONCE BETRAYING THE SANCTITY OF THE U.S. MAIL.

SAY, HENRY, ARE YOU OK?

JUST GOTTA GET SOME **AIR.** GOTTA **EAT!**

UNTIL TODAY.

HE SHOULDN'T HAVE OPENED THE **UNDELIVERED PARCEL.** BUT HE COULDN'T HELP HIMSELF.

JESUS. WHERE'D ALL THESE **BUGS** COME FROM?

FUNNY THING IS, HE CAN'T EVEN REMEMBER WHAT WAS **IN** IT.

NOW, NOTHING MATTERS BUT **FOOD.**

FOOD TO CALM THE RIOT INSIDE HIM.

GIMME SIX **MIGHTY MOUTHFULS,** GINO.

SIX? WHASSA MATTA, HENRY? YA SKIP **LUNCH?**

HE KNOWS IT WON'T BE ENOUGH.

A WHOLE **HERD** OF BURGERS -- HOOVES AND ALL -- COULDN'T FILL THE GAPING BEAK OF THE GIANT FLEDGLING THAT CRIES INSIDE HIM.

HE LUMBERS THROUGH THE EARLY EVENING STREETS, SCATTERING WRAPPERS BEHIND HIM, LIKE **SMALL CARCASSES.**

ALL IS SUBORDINATE TO HIS PRIMAL URGE FOR **FOOD.**

A FAMILIAR CLAUSTROPHOBIA ENVELOPS ME. AN AROMA OF MINGLED GREEN AND BROWN-- *STEWED CABBAGE* AND *FURNITURE POLISH.*

JUST A MINUTE, M' BOY.

I'VE GOT A *BONE* T'PICK WITH YOU.

NOT *NOW*, MRS. M. THERE'S A LUV. I'M A BIT *KNACKERED.*

I TRY NOT TO LISTEN. I DON'T *NEED* ANY *MORE* BOTHER.

NOW, I *DIDN'T* TURN HIM AWAY, 'CAUSE I *KNEW* HE WAS A FRIEND OF *YOURS.*

BUT IT'S NOT *RIGHT.* THIS IS A *RESPECTABLE* HOUSE.

WHAT *FRIEND*, MRS. M.?

ALL I WANT TO DO IS *SLEEP.*

THAT *DRUGGY* ONE. *LESTER*, OR *GARY*, I FORGET. IN A *TERRIBLE* STATE HE WAS. COME BARGING IN HERE WANTING YOU.

CHRIST-- IS HE STILL HERE?

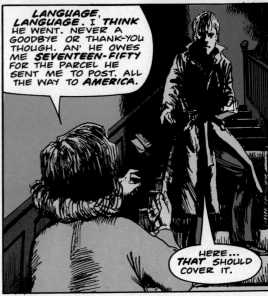

LANGUAGE, LANGUAGE. I *THINK* HE WENT. NEVER A GOODBYE OR THANK-YOU THOUGH. AN' HE OWES ME *SEVENTEEN-FIFTY* FOR THE PARCEL HE SENT ME TO POST. ALL THE WAY TO *AMERICA.*

HERE... *THAT* SHOULD COVER IT.

AS IF I HAVEN'T GOT *ENOUGH* ON M' PLATE WITH THE RUDDY *INSECTS.*

SHE MUTTERS OFF TO TORTURE MORE VEGETABLES IN HER FOUL KITCHEN.

INSECTS, EH? THAT EXPLAINS THE *RENTOKIL* VAN.

I CLIMB THE THREADBARE STAIRS. A SENSE OF *DREAD* CLIMBS WITH ME.

GARY LESTER.

WHAT DID *THAT* MESSED-UP BASTARD WANT WITH ME? HE WAS NEVER *ANYTHING* BUT...

...*BAD NEWS.*

HQ, SANCTUARY. **HOME.** I GET QUITE SENTIMENTAL ABOUT THIS PLACE, ESPECIALLY WHEN I'M AWAY.

I INHALE THE CITY'S BREATH-- RAIN-SOAKED DIESEL -- AND ADMIRE THE VIEW.

BLEEDIN' CHEERFUL POSTER.

JUST SAY

IT LOOKS LIKE A **BOMB'S** HIT IT, BUT THAT'S NORMAL. **SMELLS** BAD THOUGH. **ACRID,** MORE THAN JUST **STALE.**

THE GAS HISSES SOOTHINGLY, BUT THE ARMCHAIR NO LONGER REMEMBERS MY SHAPE.

DAMN! LAST BLOODY **FAG.** I'LL HAVE TO GO OUT.

I DECIDE TO DULL MY SENSES WITH OLD NEWS, BUT THE CRIMSON SIGNATURE OF **GARY LESTER** LIGHTS A SUDDEN FLARE OF ANGER.

THE DIRTY LOWLIFE **BASTARD!**

ALL OUT WAR

ITS FABRIC IS **GRITTY--** UNCOMFORTABLE.

I CAN'T SETTLE.

THE PULPED CONTENTS OF THE SYRINGE SET MY SKIN **CRAWLING.**

I STEEL MYSELF TO LOOK FURTHER.

INSECTS, FOR CHRIST'S SAKE. HE MUST'VE BLOODY FLIPPED!

NEVER COULD STAND NEEDLES.

MIGHTY MOUSE, THE RASTA WHO LIVES DOWNSTAIRS, RUMBLES THE FLOOR WITH HEAVY REGGAE.

I FIND THIS SOMEHOW **REASSURING.**

IN THE KITCHEN, THE STINK'S ENOUGH TO **BLIND** YOU.

DIRTY DISHES FLOUNDER IN A SARGASSO SEA OF IRIDESCENT MOLD.

NATURE HAS BEGUN HER RECLAMATION.

WITH MORBID ANTICIPATION, I APPROACH THE FRIDGE.

THE FRIDGE IS **ALWAYS** THE WORST.

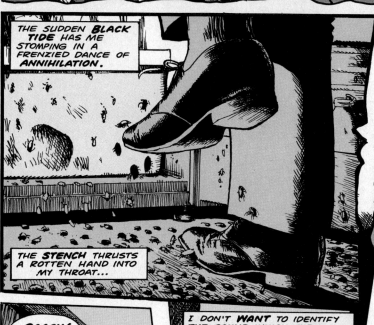

THE SUDDEN **BLACK TIDE** HAS ME STOMPING IN A FRENZIED DANCE OF **ANNIHILATION.**

THE **STENCH** THRUSTS A ROTTEN HAND INTO MY THROAT...

...AND **STRANGLES** MY STOMACH.

GAACH! I CAN DO **WITHOUT** THIS.

I DON'T **WANT** TO IDENTIFY THE SOUND WHICH TURNS ME TOWARDS THE **BATHROOM.**

SKRICH! SHIKKA! SKRASHIKKA!

COULD BE THE **PLUMBING,** I S'POSE.

BUT THAT'S JUST **WISHFUL** THINKING.

COME OUT, COME OUT, **WHATEVER** YOU ARE.

HOPE HE HASN'T O.D.'D IN THE BATH.

PURE REACTION SLAMS THE DOOR ON THE SCUTTLING HORROR. I OUGHT TO JUST WALK AWAY AND NOT COME BACK.

"DON'T LEAVE ME, JOHN."

JESUS... LORD OF THE BLOODY FLIES, EH?

I FEEL LIKE I'VE HAD MY SHARE OF BAD CRAZINESS FOR A WHILE. BUT LIKE THEY SAY--

--YOU SHOULDN'T JOIN IF YOU CAN'T TAKE A JOKE.

THE SHORT WALK TO THE CORNER SHOP CALMS ME DOWN A BIT.

THE GRAFFITI'S DEFINITELY IMPROVING.

HULLO, ALI. ALL RIGHT IF I USE THE PHONE?

OI, WATCH IT!

LEAVE IT, KENNY. THAT'S CONSTANTINE.

SOD OFF, MORON.

CHAS? JOHN. NEVER MIND WHERE I'VE BEEN. JUST PEDDLE ON 'ROUND HERE, PRONTO.

AND BRING SOME MEDICINE. I'VE GOT A SICK FRIEND. DON'T TELL ME YOUR PROBLEMS. DO IT.

WOT'S THAT STINK? CURRIED COCKROACHES? HAW HAW.

WE'LL BE BACK... PAKI!

PONDLIFE!

GIVE ME TWO HUNDRED SILK CUT, ALI -- AND SIX CANS OF BUG SPRAY. NO, BETTER MAKE IT TWELVE.

SURE, JOHN. THIS THE BEST. KILL ALL CREEPING CRAWLINGS. LIKE RAMBO. HA HA.

BACK IN THE FLAT, I'M BILLY THE KID AND GENGHIS KHAN ROLLED INTO ONE.

THIS IS IT, WILDLIFE. ARMAGEDDON FOR INSECTS.

HOLD YOUR BREATH, GAZ.

KOFF KOFF... HEUCHH.

BY THE TIME CHAS ARRIVES, THE FLAT IS A KILLING GROUND -- TINY BLACK CORPSES CRUNCH UNDERFOOT AS YOU WALK.

ALL RIGHT, MATE? YOU BRING THE GEAR?

YEAH, BUT I DON'T LIKE IT.

MNEMOTH MADE ME DO IT. SORRY, SORRY.

SO? SINCE WHEN HAVE YOU HAD SCRUPLES, CHUM? JUST STRAIGHTEN HIM OUT. I NEED ANSWERS.

THANKYOU, THANKYOU.

WHERE THE HELL'D YOU FIND THIS FREAK?

WOULD YOU BELIEVE IN THE BATH? THOUGHT HE WAS A SPIDER COME UP THE PLUGHOLE.

AAAAH.

HIS NAME'S GARY LESTER. USED TO BE A MATE OF MINE, TILL WE GOT IN SOME FUSS AND BOTHER UP IN GEORDIE LAND.

LAST I HEARD, HE WAS IN MOROCCO DOING THE WILLIAM BURROUGHS BIT. Y'KNOW, JUNK, BOYS AND GENERAL WEIRDNESS.

TIE HIM DOWN IN CASE HE FREAKS AGAIN.

I'M GOING TO PUT HIM UNDER -- FIND OUT WHAT THE SCUZZY LITTLE TOE-RAG'S BEEN UP TO.

I DON'T REALLY WANT TO KNOW, BUT WE'RE ALL JUNKIES AT HEART.

"ALL RIGHT, GAZ. JUST *RELAX*, ME OLD SON. YOU'RE FEELING *GOOD*, SO GOOD YOU WANT TO TELL ME A *STORY*..."

"...A STORY ABOUT *MNEMOTH*."

"I FEEL ROUGH, JOHN."

"*TANGIER* IS HOT. THE KIND OF HEAT THAT MAKES THE AIR *BUZZ*."

"I'M OUT IN THE *MEDINA* TRYING TO *SCORE*-- BUT I'M *BROKE*."

"IN THE MAZE OF THE OLD CITY YOU CAN WANDER FOR HOURS, RUBBING SHOULDERS WITH LIFE. EVERYONE HAS *SOMETHING* TO SELL."

YOU WANT *GIRL? BOY?* VERY CLEAN. TWENTY DIRHAM.

HAH! NO *MUHNEY*, NO *HUHNEY*.

"THE LIGHT FALLS IN PALE, GOLDEN FINGERS-- POINTING OUT DETAIL."

"THIS IS A *DREAM* PLACE, ANYTHING CAN HAPPEN."

SAFI! NO *WORK*. NO *EAT*.

MNNNNN MNNNNNG

"THEY THROW HIM OUT OF THE SWEATSHOP. HE FALLS, TWITCHING AT MY FEET."

"HE'S *MUTE*. NO *TONGUE*."

"HE'S NOT *ARAB*. MAYBE *SUDANESE*. SLAVE LABOR, I GUESS."

"I CAN SEE IT IN HIS *EYES*. JUST LIKE *NEWCASTLE*."

"*SOMETHING'S* INSIDE HIM. SOMETHING I CAN'T *RESIST*."

"I TAKE HIM *HOME*."

"IN MY ROOM, A **BLACK PASSION** SEIZES ME.

"IT'S IRRESISTIBLE.

"I WANT TO DO IT... NEED TO.

"BREATHLESS, I TIE HIM TO THE BED AND BEGIN THE **EXORCISM.**

"IT'S HORRIBLE. THE BOY **WRITHES** AND **SHAKES.**

"HIS **SKIN** STARTS TO **BLISTER.**

"THEY COME RIGHT OUT OF HIS **FLESH. THOUSANDS** OF THEM. SWARMING.

"HAVE YOU EVER HEARD A **MUTE** TRYING TO **SCREAM** ?

"OUTSIDE, THE SOUNDS OF THE STREET ARE IN ANOTHER **WORLD.**

NNNGNNNGMMMGUK

"IT FLAILS ME WITH A **MILLION WINGS.** I FEEL ITS **POWER.**

"THEN I REALIZE. IT **WANTS** TO COME OUT.

"IT TAKES ALL MY ENERGY BUT FINALLY I BIND IT. I'M TOO **STRONG** FOR IT."

"I LIGHT THE **CANDLES,** INTONE THE **CHANTS.**

"WHAT ABOUT THE KID?"

86

"MY MAGIC MOLDS IT, OVERPOWERS IT.

"THIS TIME I WIN."

"YEAH...? WHAT ABOUT THE KID?"

"THE KID? THE KID IS DEAD.

"LOOKS LIKE HE'S BEEN FLAYED.

"FLESH HANGS IN BLOODY TATTERS.

"INSIDE THE MAGIC FLASK, THE THING WRITHES LIKE SMOKE.

"I CAN FEEL IT THROUGH THE GLASS.

"IT'S HUNGRY.

"IT WANTS ME.

"THE FUNNY THING IS...

"I WANT IT.

"WANT TO FEEL IT INSIDE ME...

"SCRABBLING IN MY VEINS.

"BUT I RESIST.

"FOR ONCE, I HAVE THE POWER.

"I TRAPPED IT, JOHN.

"TRAPPED A DEMON...

...IN A BOTTLE.

"THE **HIGH** LASTS UNTIL LATE AT NIGHT -- BUT THE **COME-DOWN** IS VICIOUS.

"IT **CHOPS** MY LEGS FROM UNDER ME.

"STARK FEAR **PUNCHES** ME IN THE **GUT**.

"THE DEMON **TALKS** TO ME. A MILLION TINY, WHINING VOICES TELL ME ITS **NAME**.

"MNEMOTH.

"I **TRY** TO SHUT IT OUT, BUT IT KEEPS **ON** AND **ON**.

"PLEADING.

"THREATENING.

"IT **SINGS** OUT THE **NIGHT**...

"...AND **WHISPERS** IN THE **DAWN**.

"IT **FEELS** MY **NEED** AND **FOSTERS** IT.

"I HOLD OUT FOR ANOTHER DAY, BUT I KNOW I CAN'T HANDLE IT **ALONE**.

"I NEED **HELP**. **YOUR** HELP, JOHN.

"I MUG A TOURIST FOR HIS PASSPORT, AND SELL IT FOR THE AIR-FARE.

"AND ALL THE TIME, THE **DEAD CHILD** ON THE BED -- WITH WIDE EYES AND MOUTH -- SILENTLY CALLING **MORE** INSECTS TO A DIFFERENT FEAST.

"I **RUN**.

U.K. PASSPORT HOLDERS

"AT **HEATHROW** I AM **COLD**. MY SKIN **CRAWLS**. I HAVEN'T HAD A **FIX** FOR **DAYS**. CUSTOMS DON'T BAT AN EYELID.

"LUCK OF THE **DEVIL** I SUPPOSE.

"I HOLD ON TO HOPE. JOHN CONSTANTINE'LL KNOW WHAT TO DO."

BUT YOU'RE NOT BLOODY THERE, ARE YOU?

"I BLAG MY WAY INTO YOUR PAD, THEN GO OUT TO GET SOME JUNK SO'S I CAN THINK STRAIGHT."

ALL RIGHT, MATE. CALM DOWN. I'M HERE NOW.

THWAK

"BUT THE SCENE'S CHANGED. EVERYTHING'S DIFFERENT NOW.

"IT MAKES ME LOCK MYSELF IN. MAKES ME A PRISONER.

"IT WORKS ON ME CONSTANTLY, PROMISING ME FREEDOM; FROM FEAR, FROM PAIN; IF ONLY I WILL GIVE IT THE SAME RELEASE.

"I'M CRAZY-- AND THE INSECTS HAVE STARTED TO ARRIVE.

"I'M ON THE EDGE, AND THE EDGE IS CRUMBLING.

"IT MAKES ME DO WEIRD, DARK THINGS.

"IF I DON'T GET RID OF IT, I KNOW IT'LL KILL ME.

"THE OLD GIRL SAYS SHE THINKS YOU'RE IN THE STATES. I REMEMBER YOUR FRIEND, EMMA.

"SO I SEND IT TO YOU THERE.

"JOHN CONSTANTINE'LL KNOW WHAT TO DO, I THINK.

"JOHN'LL KNOW."

I KNOW WHAT I'D **LIKE** TO DO WITH THE USELESS BASTARD. KICK HIS ARSE **OUT** OF HERE AND GET SOME **KIP.**

I COULD TAKE 'IM AND... ER... **DUMP** 'IM SOMEWHERE, JOHN.

NAH. IT'S A **BLOODY** 'ORRIBLE MESS, BUT I S'POSE I'D BETTER SORT IT OUT.

CHAS, IN THAT DRAWER GET US A PAPER AND PEN.

RIGHT THEN, GAZ. YOU CAN **REST** SOON, BUT **FIRST** I WANT YOU TO DRAW THE MUTE KID. BONE STRUCTURE, TATTOOS, THE LOT.

HMMM... NOT BAD. YOU SHOULD HAVE STUCK IT OUT AT **ART SCHOOL** INSTEAD OF PONCING ABOUT WITH **MAGIC.**

NOW **SLEEP.**

ER... YOU FINISHED WIV **ME** THEN, JOHN?

I KNOW I WON'T **SLEEP.** I LIGHT A FAG AND CHECK THE STREET.

THE GIRL WITH THE SPRAY CAN'S GOOD. REMINDS ME OF **EMMA.** BUT EMMA'S ON THE OTHER SIDE OF THE WORLD...

OH, **NO,** CHUM. **YOU'D** BETTER GO AND PICK UP THREE DAYS WORTH OF FOOD, FAGS, AND DIRTY BOOKS. **YOU'RE** GOING TO BE DOING A SPOT OF **BABY-SITTING.**

BUT I...

NO **BUTS,** MATE. YOU **OWE** ME.

AND SHE'S **DEAD.**

THE PROFESSOR'S AN *ANTHROPOLOGIST* AND A BIT OF A *DABBLER* IN THE OCCULT.

WHAT IS THIS PLACE, PLEASE?

THE *BRITISH MUSEUM*, CHUM. TREASURE HOUSE OF THE *EMPIRE*. WHERE WE KEEP ALL THE *LOOT*.

A BIT *BARMY*, BUT HE KNOWS HIS STUFF.

WHAT D'YOU *RECKON* THEN, PROF?

INTERESTING... YES. I'VE SEEN SIMILAR TATTOOS IN *SOUTHERN SUDAN*.

ONLY *ONE* TRIBE STILL PRACTICING *THIS* KIND OF *SACRIFICIAL* MAGIC, AS FAR AS I *KNOW*.

"A BRANCH OF THE *DINKA* PEOPLE. THE TATTOOS ARE A SPELL OF *BINDING*, OR *CONTAINMENT*.

"THE *SHAMAN* MUST BE A *MASTER* OF ELEMENTAL MAGIC."

SEEMS TO MAKE SENSE. *MOROCCO? SUDAN?* BETTER PACK ME *PITH HELMET.*

I PHONE *NEW YORK*.

MIDNITE'S A *HAITIAN HEAVYWEIGHT*. FANCIES HIMSELF AS THE *PAPA DOC OF CRIME*. GOOD MAGICIAN, THOUGH. I LIKE TO WIND HIM UP.

HELLO, POPS... CONSTANTINE.

LISTEN, THIS IS *IMPORTANT*.

IS ANYTHING *WEIRD* GOING DOWN? Y'KNOW, ANY FUNNY *BUGS* IN THE *BIG APPLE*?

YEAH..? STARVED IN A *RESTAURANT*?

OH, JUST A *HUNCH*. GOTTA RUN NOW. SAY HELLO TO THE SKULLS FOR ME. HA HA HA.

THAT PAPA MIDNITE, *NO* SENSE OF HUMOR. HIS VOICE SOUNDS LIKE IT COULD *GRIND BONES*. LOOKS LIKE THIS *MNEMOTH'S* OUT AND ABOUT IN NYC THEN.

AFRICA FIRST, THOUGH. FIND OUT WHAT'S *WHAT*.

OXFA

TAXI

NEW

'FRAID THAT'S A *BIT* OUT OF MY *WAY*, GUV...

91

YESTERDAY I WAS *SHIVERING* IN *LONDON*. NOW THE SUDANESE SUN SCORCHES THE SKIN FROM ME, LIKE A *BLOWTORCH*.

HOPE THERE'S NO *GUERRILLAS*. DON'T WANT TO WIND UP AS A *HOSTAGE*. IT'S ALREADY COST ME AN INDUSTRIALIST'S RANSOM TO GET *THIS* FAR.

WE *WALK* NOW. TWO, THREE HOURS.

RIGHTO. *MAD DOGS* AND *ENGLISHMEN*, EH?

THIS IS ANOTHER *WORLD*. I FEEL LIKE A *SPACEMAN*.

IT TAKES *FIVE* HOURS. AS THE SUN WOBBLES DOWN ONTO THE HORIZON, SPILLING ITS BLOOD ACROSS THE PLAIN, LIKE A *WOUNDED ANIMAL*...

TOO MUCH *SUN*, BOSS?

...WE *FIND* THE VILLAGE.

THEY WATCH ME *STRANGELY* AND IN *SILENCE*. I SHOW THEM LESTER'S PORTRAIT OF THE *MUTE*.

THE *GUIDE* JABBERS IN RAPID DINKA, BUT I HAVE ALREADY *SEEN* THE SPARK OF RECOGNITION...

... THE QUICK GLANCE OF COAL-BLACK EYES TOWARDS THE *HILL*...

HELLO. ANYBODY *HOME*?

...AND THE HUT WHICH STANDS *ALONE*.

ENTER. I HAD EXPECTED YOU *SOONER*. THE ENTRAILS OF THE SHE-GOAT 'NDICATED *YESTERDAY* AS THE TIME OF ARRIVAL.

YEAH? WELL, YOU CAN'T RELY ON *ANYTHING* THESE DAYS, CAN YOU?

WHERE'D YOU LEARN YOUR *ENGLISH* THEN?

YOU *HEAR* ENGLISH. I DO NOT *SPEAK* ENGLISH...

THAT'S *NEAT.* THE *PENTECOST EFFECT.* YOU COULD GET A JOB AT THE *UNITED NATIONS.*

I *KNOW* YOU NOW. YOU ARE THE *LAUGHING MAGICIAN.* I DREAMT YOU ONCE.

YEAH? HOPE YOU DIDN'T WAKE UP *SCREAMING.*

IS IT *TRUE?* THE *HUNGER SPIRIT* IS *LOOSE* AGAIN? THE *SACRIFICE* WAS IN *VAIN?*

'FRAID *SO,* OLD *SON.*

AND YOU WOULD LEARN TO *BIND* IT AGAIN?

WELL, I *WAS* SORT OF HOPING TO *PERSUADE YOU.* I MEAN YOU *DO* KNOW *HOW* -- DON'T YOU..?

IT IS NOT POSSIBLE. MY *POWER* IS TIED TO THIS PLACE -- THIS *EARTH.*

BUT IF YOU ARE *STRONG* ENOUGH, WE COULD SHARE A VISION OF WHAT HAS *BEEN* AND COULD *BE* AGAIN...

I'M *GAME* FOR A LAUGH, YEAH.

WE CHEW.

THE ROOT IS *BITTER* AND DROPS INTO MY *EMPTY* STOMACH LIKE *GOBBETS* OF MOLTEN LAVA.

WITHIN MOMENTS MY HEAD IS *ERUPTING* -- SMEARING REALITY UP THE WALLS.

CHRIST. I HATE PSYCHEDELICS.

HE FIDDLES WITH HIS FACE. HIS OTHER HAND RUSHES ME LIKE AN *EXPRESS TRAIN.*

SURELY HE WON'T...

TERROR EXPLODES INTO A SUDDEN AGONY OF BLACKNESS AS HE TAKES MY EYE.

REPLACING IT WITH THE *SOFT FRUIT* TORN FROM HIS OWN BODY.

A SCALDING PAIN CUTS A RED LINE THROUGH BLACK.

THROUGH WHITE.

IN STATIONARY SUFFERING, THE SILENT STARVING ACCUSE ME.

I KNOW I MUST DO BATTLE FOR THE PEOPLE.

BUT IT IS HARD TO *CHOOSE.* THEY ARE ALL MY CHILDREN.

THEY LOOK TO ME FOR PROTECTION.

THEIR FEAR, THEIR *HUNGER,* HAS GIVEN THE SPIRIT *STRENGTH.*

MNEMOTH FEEDS ON THEM-- GROWS *STRONGER* AS THEY WEAKEN.

I TAKE HIM TO THE *PLACE OF POWER,*

AND CUT OUT HIS TONGUE SO THAT HE MAY NOT *CURSE* WE WHO *BETRAY* HIM.

94

WE RUN TOGETHER AND SPREAD OUT INTO MEMORY.

WHY DOES PRIMITIVE MAGIC ALWAYS HURT!

THERE ARE FLIES DRINKING FROM THE EYES OF CHILDREN.

FLIES IN THE EYES OF FLIES.

I BREATHE THE SCENT OF FLESH, BROILED BY THE PITILESS SUN IN A BROTH OF DISEASE AND DEATH.

AT MY CALL THE SPIRIT RISES FROM THE LAND LIKE SMOKE.

MY MAGIC BENDS HIM AND HE ENTERS MY SOFT TRAP.

GUNNNNNNGG

WHILE THE BOY WRITHES WITH THE TORMENT OF MNEMOTH'S HUNGER--

--I CUT THE POWER PATTERNS OF BINDING INTO BLACK SKIN STRETCHED TAUT OVER HEAVING RIBS.

WHEN IT IS DONE, I TAKE HIM FAR AWAY, TO THE BARREN PLACE.

HERE THE SPIRIT WILL CONSUME HIM AND SO, CONSUME ITSELF.

I WALK AWAY. I DO NOT LOOK BACK.

THIS PART I DIDN'T KNOW. BUSH-FIGHTERS FOUND HIM AND SOLD HIM TO SLAVERS FOR TOBACCO.

I AM A *FOOL.* I SHOULD HAVE STAYED TO OVERSEE HIS END.

YEAH, WELL. *NEVER LOOK BACK'S* A GOOD MOTTO IN *OUR* LINE OF BUSINESS.

TOO MANY BLOODY *GHOSTS* FOLLOWING.

THE DRUG HAS SCREWED ME UP *ROYALLY.* MY GUTS ARE IN AN *UPROAR* BUT I GET THE FEELING I OUGHT TO HURRY.

I WOBBLE DOWN THE HILL ON LEGS LIKE BITS OF *ROPE.*

THE OLD BOY WAS SHREWD. HIS SHOCK TACTICS WERE A BIT CRUDE BUT THEY WORKED.

I KNOW WHAT I'VE GOT TO DO.

YEAH, NO FLIES ON HIM.

THE DAY AFTER AND I'M *STILL* HUNG-OVER. BUT IT'S UP, UP AND AWAY TO PICK UP *LESTER* -- THEN ON TO THE *STATES.*

IT'S A GAME... ENNIT?

THE AFRICAN SKY IS ENDLESS BLUE. BELOW, OUR SHADOW *SCYTHES* A CITY OF TENTS.

TINY BLACK DOTS MOVE AMONGST THEM -- LIKE INSECTS.

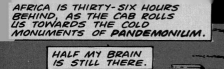

AFRICA IS THIRTY-SIX HOURS BEHIND, AS THE CAB ROLLS US TOWARDS THE COLD MONUMENTS OF *PANDEMONIUM.*

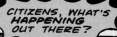

THE DJ'S VOICE IS LIKE A ROLLER COASTER.

HALF MY BRAIN IS STILL THERE.

JET LAG.

ELASTIC TIME.

CITIZENS, WHAT'S *HAPPENING* OUT THERE?

REMEMBER THE GUY WHO *STARVED* IN A RESTAURANT?

AND THE BOSS WHO TRIED TO *EAT* HIS SECRETARY?

WELL TODAY, HORRIFIED SHOPPERS WATCH AS BRUCE PARKER FATALLY CRAMS HIMSELF WITH GEMSTONES IN HIS 57TH STREET STORE WINDOW!

ONLY IN *NEW YORK,* FOLKS. STAY TUNED. YOU NEED TO *KNOW.*

FREAKIN' *WEIRDOS.* FIRST WE GOT *CANCER.* THEN WE GOT *AIDS.* NOW WHAT THE HELL WE GOT?

I CAN'T BE BOTHERED TO TELL HIM.

MNEMOTH'S *HERE,* ISN'T IT, JOHN?

I'M *SCARED.*

AND THIS WHINING BASTARD HASN'T SHUT UP SINCE HEATHROW.

I COULD CHEERFULLY *CROAK* HIM.

WILL THIS *PAPA MIDNITE* HAVE ANY *GEAR,* JOHN?

I REALLY *NEED* IT, MAN.

S'POSE IT'S *EASIER* TO FEEL THAT WAY.

PAPA MIDNITE'S CLUB IN MANHATTAN IS DEFINITELY *HIGH RENT*.

I'D HAVE MORE CHANCE OF GETTING AN *ALLIGATOR* THROUGH THE FRONT DOOR THAN GARY LESTER.

IT'LL HAVE TO BE THE SERVICE ENTRANCE.

ARE WE GOING TO GET THE *JUNK* NOW, JOHN?

THIS MAN HAS GOT TO BE *TOLD*.

I COUNT TEN PACES TO THE BASEMENT GARAGE.

THEN I *SNAP*.

STOP GOING ON ABOUT *DOPE!*

WHA!

BECAUSE *YOU ARE* A *STUPID, WEAK CRETIN* WHO CAN'T RESIST *SCREWING* HIMSELF UP, *WE* ARE ON THE VERGE OF *MASS DEMONIC POSSESSION* IN ONE OF THE *FOREMOST* POPULATION CENTERS OF THE *GLOBE!*

DON'T *HURT* ME.

TEMPER, JOHN, TEMPER.

PATHETIC SOD.

SORRY, I'M A BIT WOBBLY.

YEAH, WELL, YOU'D BETTER KEEP IT TOGETHER WITH OLD *MIDNITE*, MATE.

STAR ON

HE'S A BIT OF A *TASTY GEEZER.*

HE'S INTO A LOT OF WEIRD STUFF. THIS CLUB FRONTS AN ILLEGAL GAMBLING JOINT -- I TOOK HIM FOR FIFTY THOU LAST YEAR.

CLIK!

THEN THERE'S THE *ARENA*, THAT'S FOR THE REAL *SICKOS.*

C'MON.

YOU TELL ME YOU DO NOT *KNOW* IT?

SISTER, I THOUGHT *YOUR* INTIMACY EMBRACED *ALL* THE DEMONS OF HELL.

DR. ARNOLD, REVEREND BANSTRINGER, I MUST INTERRUPT YOU. REPORTS ARE COMING IN OF ANOTHER *CRAMMER* INCIDENT...

NEWBORN AND *HUNGRY*, IS IT?

THEN WE MUST MAKE SURE IT DINES *ELSEWHERE*.

IN THE BRONX, A THIRTY-YEAR-OLD MAN HAS GORGED HIMSELF TO DEATH ON A COLLECTION OF *RARE* COMICBOOKS...

SERVANT. BRING ME A *WHITE* FOWL.

HE CAN BE A BIT *BLOODTHIRSTY* AT TIMES, LIKE ALL YOUR *VOODOO* TYPES.

HE'S A PRETTY SPOOKY GUY.

ELEVATOR'S DOWN HERE, I THINK.

YEAH. PACKS A LOT OF CLOUT DOES OLD MIDNITE.

JESUS! WHAT'S THAT SMELL? WORSE THAN A BLOODY *ZOO*!

AH, 'SCUSE *US*.

WHAT DO YOU *WANT,* CONSTANTINE?

WOULD YOU BELIEVE *HELP*?

"THE INDIANS SAY, WHEN THE TIGER FEEDS THE JUNGLE HOLDS ITS BREATH."

"IF THIS CITY HOLDS *ITS* BREATH, IT WON'T BE PUTTING ITS MONEY IN YOUR POCKET."

YOU *CHEAT* ME OUT OF FIFTY-THOUSAND DOLLARS, THEN ASK FOR *HELP!*

YOU HAVE *SATAN'S* NERVE.

FORGET ABOUT THE *MONEY,* MIDNITE. I'M TALKING ABOUT THE *REAL* WORLD.

THE ONE WHERE THE HUNGER SPIRIT, *MNEMOTH,* IS BUSY *MUNCHING* ITS WAY THROUGH THE POPULATION.

IT'S OUT *THERE,* MIDNITE. OR PERHAPS YOU HADN'T *NOTICED*?

THINK ABOUT IT, POPS. CAN A MAN OF POWER *AFFORD* TO HAVE A *DEMON* RAMPAGING THROUGH HIS GARDEN?

I KNOW HOW TO *BEAT* IT. BUT I NEED HELP FROM A MAGICIAN-- A *STRONG* ONE.

I'LL CONSIDER IT.

YOU DO THAT, MATE. ASK THE **SKULLS** ABOUT IT. I'LL BE BACK LATER.

KEEP AN EYE ON MY FRIEND HERE, AND GIVE MY LOVE TO YOUR **SISTER**. SHE WAS AN AMAZING WOMAN.

SHE STILL IS.

SEE YA.

HE'S AN EDGY BASTARD, BUT I THINK HE'LL COME 'ROUND. PLAYED TO HIS **VANITY** JUST ENOUGH.

ER, MR. MIDNITE? JOHN SAID YOU MIGHT HELP ME TO GET **STRAIGHT**, LIKE..?

DID HE?

WHAT DO YOU **NEED**?

H...HEROIN.

HMMM, MAYBE LATER.

FIRST, TELL ME ABOUT YOUR STRANGE FRIEND. HAVE YOU KNOWN HIM LONG?

DO YOU **TRUST** HIM?

ARRK!

"I TRUST JOHN WITH MY **LIFE**."

IN THE LIFT, COMING DOWN, I GET THE SHAKES.

PAPA MIDNITE HAS THAT EFFECT ON YOU.

OUTSIDE, IT'S RAINING. NO CABS. 'SFUNNY. WASN'T RAINING UP THERE.

MUST'VE BEEN ABOVE THE CLOUDS.

DOWN ON THE SUBWAY, I'M SQUEEZED BY WET AND PUNGENT FLESH.

WE SHARE EACH OTHER'S FETID AIR.

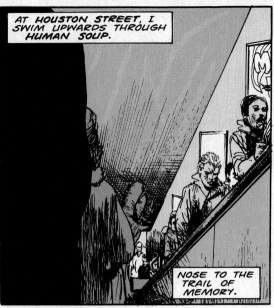

AT HOUSTON STREET, I SWIM UPWARDS THROUGH HUMAN SOUP.

NOSE TO THE TRAIL OF MEMORY.

TURNING ALL THE FAMILIAR GREENWICH VILLAGE CORNERS IS SATISFYINGLY PAINFUL.

LIKE PICKING SCABS.

BUT, BY THE TIME I REACH HER BUILDING, I'VE DRAWN BLOOD.

I DON'T WANT TO GO INSIDE.

MUST'VE LANDED ABOUT HERE.

I'VE GOT TO CHECK IT OUT. THIS IS WHERE THAT PRATT LESTER POSTED THE HUNGER SPIRIT.

TO EMMA'S PLACE, HE SAID.

STUDIO LIGHT'S ON. SHE'D BE WORKING LATE.

IF SHE WASN'T DEAD.

IF THE GODDAMNED INVUNCHE HADN'T THROWN HER OUT OF THE BLOODY WINDOW.

THE SMELL FROM THE LOFT NEARLY **CONJURES** HER.

OILS, TURPS, PAINT.

SHE ALWAYS HAD A SMUDGE OF PAINT ON HER ELBOW.

YEAH?

I'M A FRIEND OF EMMA'S. MIND IF I COME IN?

SHE DOESN'T LIVE HERE ANYMORE, MAN.

I WONDER IF SHE **SCREAMED**? HOW **LONG** DID IT TAKE?

YEAH, SHE'S DEAD. DID YOU KNOW HER?

NOT VERY WELL, BUT HER DEATH SEEMS TO HAVE **INSPIRED** ME.

WELL, CHUM, IT'S AN **ILL WIND**, AS THEY SAY.

NO DEMONS HERE. ONLY ECHOES.

'SWEIRD, I'VE BEEN WORKING ON **THIS** SINCE I MOVED IN.

A WRITHING BITTERNESS RISES IN MY THROAT AND TRIES TO CHOKE MY WORDS. I REMEMBER HER **SOFTNESS**, AND THE **RAW VIOLENCE** OF THE INVUNCHE.

THE **HAIR COLOR'S** WRONG, PAL.

TIME I WAS GONE. NOTHING HERE BUT NIGHTMARES.

NAH, JUST ONE PARCEL. I SENT IT BACK TO THE POST OFFICE.

SHE EVER GET ANY **MAIL**?

'BYE, EMMA. SORRY, LUV.

ON THE LANDING, MY HEAD STARTS TO EXPLODE, SLOWLY.

I'M TOO CLOSE TO THIS THING. I'M BLOWING IT.

HI, JOHN.

NO FOOD. NO SLEEP.

AND I DIDN'T NEED TO SEE THAT PICTURE.

THE SUDDEN VOICE JOLTS ME OVER THE EDGE.

IT'S A BAD CASE OF MENTAL WHEELSPIN.

I STRUGGLE FOR TRACTION--

EMMA?

--AND FAIL.

EMMA IS DEAD. BUT EMMA IS TALKING TO ME. I CAN HEAR HER.

YOU DON'T LOOK VERY PLEASED TO SEE ME.

H...HOW ARE YOU?

--THEREFORE, EMMA IS ALIVE, EMMA IS A GHOST, OR I'VE FLIPPED.

DEAD, SMARTASS. HOW D'YOU THINK?

I S'POSE IT WAS A STUPID QUESTION.

RAWWRUNCH!

THE BLOKE TAKES A FEW MINUTES TO DIE.

WE LAP UP THE GORY DETAILS.

THE THING IS NEAR. I'M TENSE, ITCHING TO FIGHT.

FOLLOW THE BEE AND FIND THE HIVE, THEY SAY.

WONDER IF IT WORKS WITH FLIES.

IT DOES.

HERE WE GO THEN.

I'M THE HUNTER AND I'M HUNGRY.

IT DOES ME GOOD TO RUN.

THROUGH THE DARK.

THROUGH THE RAIN.

IF IT WASN'T FOR EMMA IT WOULD'VE HAD ME. I OWE HER, AGAIN.

WHILE I RUN, I THINK OF THE PRIEST.

FINALLY, MY LUNGS GIVE OUT.

KOFF KOFF KOFFF

SHE WAS RIGHT. IT'S MUCH TOO STRONG FOR ME.

HAVE TO MOVE FAST NOW.

I'M GOING TO NEED MIDNITE AND I'M GOING TO NEED GARY LESTER.

POOR BASTARD.'

CONTINUED IN THE TRADE PAPERBACK COLLECTION *ORIGINAL SINS*.

HOLD ME

Neil Gaiman
WRITER

Dave McKean
ARTIST

Dave McKean
Daniel Vozzo
COLORISTS

Todd Klein
LETTERER

Dave McKean
COVER ARTIST

IT WAS FAT RONNIE'S IDEA.

IT WAS SO COLD THAT SPRING.

FAT RONNIE AND SYLVIA FROM HULL
USED TO HANG AROUND TOGETHER,
AND SOMEWHERE ALONG THE WAY
JACKO WOUND UP WANDERING WITH THEM.

SO WHEN THE OLD BILL CAME ROUND
WITH THEIR BLOODY HOSES AT THREE
IN THE MORNING, WHEN THEY'D JUST
GOT SETTLED UNDER THE BRIDGE...

WHY THEN FAT RONNIE SAID, "SOD THIS
FOR A GAME OF SOLDIERS. (GI'SSA SWIG
YA BASTARD.) LET'S GO FIND US
SOMEWHERE WARM."

THEY SNUCK AROUND THE ESTATE LIKE SHABBY RATS, PASSING THE BOTTLE FROM HAND TO HAND.

THEY FOUND THEIR BOLT-HOLE ON THE FOURTH FLOOR. NO LIGHT OR POWER, NO FOOD; STILL, SOMEWHERE TO BE, SOMEWHERE TO HIDE UNTIL THINGS GOT WARMER.

IT WAS SO VERY COLD THAT SPRING.

hold me

2

FAT RONNIE AND SYLVIA FROM HULL RIPPED DOWN A CURTAIN, WRAPPED IT AROUND THEMSELVES, HELD EACH OTHER FOR WARMTH.

JACKO KNEW IT WAS TOO COLD EVEN FOR THAT. AND THERE WAS NO ONE TO HOLD JACKO ANYWAY.

ICE-CRYSTALS GLITTERED ON THE WINDOW GLASS, AND THE LIGHTS OF LONDON BURNED CLEAR AND COLD IN THE DARKNESS.

HE HAD TO GET AWAY. HE HAD TO HIDE.

HE HAD TO GET WARM.

THIS WAS HIS DOSS, AND HE WAS BUGGERED IF ANYONE WAS GOING TO TAKE IT AWAY FROM HIM.

AUTUMN IN THE SMOKE.

DON'T YOU JUST LOVE IT TO DEATH? WHEN THE LEAVES START TO CRISP AND YELLOW, AND THE MISTS CRAWL IN OFF THE THAMES, AND ALL THE GOOD-LOOKING WOMEN VANISH.

I WAS CHATTING TO THIS CAB DRIVER THE OTHER DAY. HE SAID HE THOUGHT THE PRETTY ONES IN THE SUMMER DRESSES WERE LIKE BUTTERFLIES.

HE SAID WHEN IT GETS COLD THEY GO OFF AND HIBERNATE IN EMPTY ROOMS. S'POSE HE MUST HAVE BEEN A FRUSTRATED POET, OR A HORROR WRITER.

THIS ONE SEEMS TO BE A NATIONAL FRONT RECRUITER.

WELL, I MEAN, THEY'RE NOT *LIKE US*, ARE THEY? STANDS TO *REASON*.

THEY'RE CERTAINLY NOT LIKE YOU.

NAH, I MEAN, OLD *ENOCH*, *HE* HAD THE RIGHT IDEA. SHOULD HAVE *SENT* THEM ALL BACK TO *BONGO-BONGO* LAND. 'ERE, I HEARD THIS *TRIFFIC* WOG JOKE THE OTHER WEEK...

CHRIST! I CAN'T STAND ANY MORE OF THIS.

STOP THE TAXI...

BUT *THIS* ISN'T HAWTHORNE ROAD!

TOO RIGHT. BUT THE WALK'LL DO ME GOOD, EH? HERE YOU GO. TWO POUNDS THIRTY.

DON'T I GET A *TIP?*

SURE. IT'S THIS: GET A NEW MIND. THE ONE YOU'VE GOT NOW IS NARROW, AND FULL OF CRAP.

HE SHOUTS OBSCENITIES AT ME AS HE DRIVES AWAY.

GOING TO A SMALL DO IN EAST LONDON: IT'S A YEAR SINCE RAY MONDE KICKED IT, AND SOME OF HIS MATES ARE GETTING TOGETHER TO PARTY IN HIS MEMORY.

HE ALWAYS LOVED A PARTY, DID RAY.

EXCUSE ME. COULD I, UH, I'M SORRY, COULD I POSSIBLY TROUBLE YOU FOR A CIGARETTE?

SURE.

YOU DOSSING OUT HERE, THEN?

MMM. THERE'S QUITE A FEW OF US ROUND HERE. IT WAS OKAY IN THE SUMMER, BUT I HATE THE COLD.

YEAH?

YES. AND DRUNK YUPPIES. COUPLE OF THEM WORKED ME OVER THE OTHER NIGHT.

I'M SORRY.

ME TOO.

SEEMS LIKE THERE DIDN'T USED TO BE SO MANY HOMELESS ON THE STREETS.

I GAVE HIM A QUID AND SOME CIGARETTES, AND HE SEEMED PATHETICALLY GRATEFUL.

BREAKS YOUR *HEART,* DUNNIT?

JOHN! SOOOO PLEASED YOU COULD MAKE IT! GRAB A *DRINK* FROM THE LOUNGE, THEN COME OVER HERE -- SOMEONE I *DESPERATELY* WANT YOU TO *MEET.*

ANTHEA -- JOHN CONSTANTINE. THE ONE I WAS TELLING YOU ABOUT-- OUR *FAVORITE* MAN OF MYSTERY.

NOW JOHN, ANTHEA WAS A *DEAR* FRIEND OF RAY'S.

HULLO ANTHEA.

HELLO JOHN.

MAYBE I'M GETTING SOUR IN ME OLD AGE, BUT I DON'T SEEM TO ENJOY PARTIES LIKE I USED TO. EVERYBODY TRYING DESPERATELY TO HAVE FUN.

IT DIDN'T USED TO BE SO MUCH EFFORT... DID IT?

I'M *SORRY,* RAY. WASN'T MY FAULT, THOUGH, MATE. YOU *KNEW* THAT. *DIDN'T* YOU?

YOU WAIT HERE, LOVE, OKAY?

OKAY, JOHN.

SHE'S DEAD. I CAN TELL FROM HERE. FROM WHAT THE KIDDIE SAYS, SHE CAN'T HAVE BEEN DEAD MORE THAN A FEW HOURS.

BUT SHE'S SO *COLD.* FEELS LIKE SHE'S JUST BEEN HAULED OUT OF A FREEZER.

THIS ISN'T NATURAL.

THIS IS NASTY.

IS MY MUMMY ALL RIGHT, JOHN?

NO, LOVE. SHE'S NOT.

HAS SHE GONE TO THE BABY JESUS?

SOMETHING LIKE THAT, LOVE. SOMETHING LIKE THAT.

KNOCK KNOCK!

WELL, YOU CAN JUST SOD OFF, JOHN CONSTANTINE...

OH. IT'S YOU.

NAH.

I GOT A PRESENT FOR YOU. SHE'S NOT A BLONDE, AND I DON'T KNOW HOW LONG YOU GET TO KEEP HER.

HER NAME'S SHONA.

IF I'M NOT BACK IN HALF AN HOUR, CALL THE POLICE -- FAT LOT OF GOOD THEY'LL BE -- AND AN AMBULANCE FOR HER MUM. FLAT 510.

BUT SHOULDN'T I CALL AN AMBULANCE NOW? IF HER MOTHER'S ILL...

HER MUM'S DEAD, ANTHEA, NOT SICK. IT WON'T MAKE ANY DIFFERENCE...

HALF AN HOUR.

YOU KNOW, I NEVER MET A PADLOCK I COULDN'T OPEN WITH FIVE MINUTES AND A BENT PAPERCLIP...

OR FIVE SECONDS AND A SLEDGE HAMMER... BUT YOU TAKE WHAT YOU CAN GET, DON'T YOU?

EUUGH.

I DON'T KNOW WHAT I'M DOING HERE. COMMON SENSE SAYS THAT I SHOULD BE HALFWAY HOME RIGHT NOW.

WHAT AM I TRYING TO PROVE?

JOHN CONSTANTINE, YOU CAN BE A REAL PRAT SOMETIMES.

HELLO? ANYONE HERE?

IT'S SO COLD.

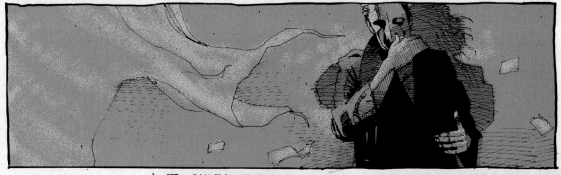

ALL HE WANTED.

ALL HE WANTED WAS FOR SOMEONE TO CARE ABOUT HIM. SOMEONE TO HOLD HIM. SOMEONE TO WARM HIM.

NOBODY WOULD.

WHEN WE HOLD EACH OTHER, IN THE DARKNESS, IT DOESN'T MAKE THE DARKNESS GO AWAY. THE BAD THINGS ARE STILL OUT THERE. THE NIGHTMARES ARE STILL WALKING.

WHEN WE HOLD EACH OTHER, WE FEEL-- NOT SAFE, BUT BETTER. "IT'S ALL RIGHT," WE WHISPER. "I'M HERE. I LOVE YOU." AND WE LIE, "I'LL NEVER LEAVE YOU."

FOR JUST A MOMENT OR TWO THE DARKNESS DOESN'T SEEM SO BAD. WHEN WE HOLD EACH OTHER.

JOHN? ARE YOU ALL RIGHT? WHAT'S HAPPENED? GOD-- YOU SMELL AWFUL. WHAT'S THE MATTER?

ANTHEA. PLEASE. SHUT UP.

JUST HOLD ME.

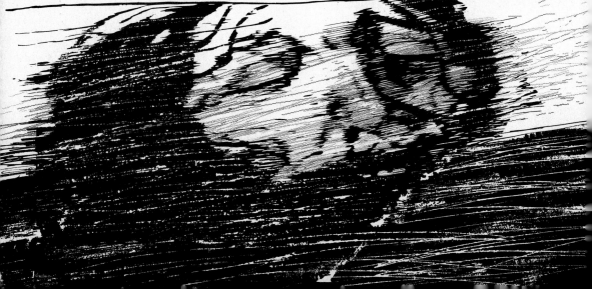

THE BEGINNING OF THE END

Garth Ennis
WRITER

Will Simpson
PENCILLER

Mark Pennington
INKER

Tom Ziuko
COLORIST

Gaspar Saladino
LETTERER

Tom Canty
COVER ARTIST

SPRINGTIME.

EVERYTHING WAKES UP AND GETS ON WITH IT.

EVERYTHING CARRIES ON LIVING.

ALL EXCEPT FOR ME.

I'M DYING.

BUT THE PATH ISN'T SUPPOSED TO END HERE...

LIKE THIS...

IS IT?

I SHOULD DIE AS I LIVED.

SOMEDAY I WOULD PUSH IT TOO FAR. GET TOO CLEVER. THE JAWS OF HELL WOULD SNAP SHUT AND FOR ONCE I'D BE THAT LITTLE BIT TOO SLOW.

MY DEATH WOULD BE UNIQUE.

THAT ISN'T REALLY THE PROBLEM, THOUGH. MAYBE I'M STILL STUPID ENOUGH TO BELIEVE IT MATTERS THAT MY DEATH WILL BE SO...ORDINARY...

BUT THAT'S NOT REALLY THE PROBLEM.

THE PROBLEM IS SIMPLY THIS:

I'M DYING.

I SUPPOSE I'VE BEEN DYING FOR SOME TIME, NOW...

STRANGE I ONLY FOUND OUT LAST **WEEK**.

UUUCCH...

JESUS.

WHAT THE FU--

HUCCCHHH... PROOOCCH!

CHRIST ALMI-- PROOOOCCHHH!

I REMEMBER THINKING THERE WAS SO MUCH... *TOO* MUCH...

TOO MUCH FOR A BIT LIP OR A CUT GUM OR A SORE THROAT, AND IT SURE AS HELL WASN'T GOING TO CLEAR UP BY LUNCHTIME.

I WAS JUST WONDERING WHAT IT *REALLY* WAS WHEN CONFUSION TURNED TO *FEAR* ...

AT FIRST I THOUGHT I WAS *CHOKING.*

HUULLCHUULP!

THIS TIME IT WASN'T BLOOD, AND IT WASN'T SNOT.

WASN'T EVEN LIQUID.

I'D JUST SPAT A PIECE OF MYSELF INTO THE SINK.

I STARTED THINKING FAST, RUNNING THROUGH THE POSSIBILITIES...

THE DEMON BLOOD? NERGAL WORKING SOME KIND OF REVENGE, ROBBING ME OF VICTORY TWO YEARS ON?

THAT WAS OBVIOUS, WASN'T IT?

OR MAYBE SOMETHING ELSE, ALMOST TOO STRANGE TO THINK ABOUT--

MY TWIN.

MY MEMORIES OF LAST AUTUMN IN THE WOMB-CAVE ARE HAZY... DID MY PERFECT BROTHER MERGE WITH ME, TURNING US INTO SOMETHING BETTER?

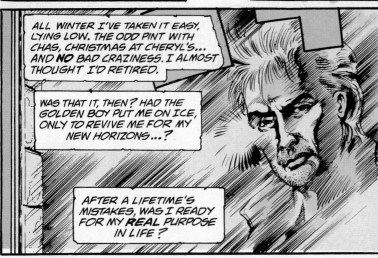
ALL WINTER I'VE TAKEN IT EASY, LYING LOW. THE ODD PINT WITH CHAS, CHRISTMAS AT CHERYL'S... AND NO BAD CRAZINESS. I ALMOST THOUGHT I'D RETIRED.

WAS THAT IT, THEN? HAD THE GOLDEN BOY PUT ME ON ICE, ONLY TO REVIVE ME FOR MY NEW HORIZONS...?

AFTER A LIFETIME'S MISTAKES, WAS I READY FOR MY REAL PURPOSE IN LIFE?

TO DIE?

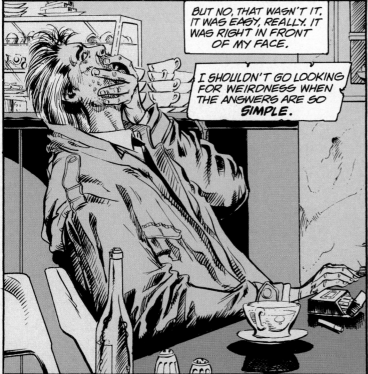
BUT NO, THAT WASN'T IT. IT WAS EASY, REALLY. IT WAS RIGHT IN FRONT OF MY FACE.

I SHOULDN'T GO LOOKING FOR WEIRDNESS WHEN THE ANSWERS ARE SO SIMPLE.

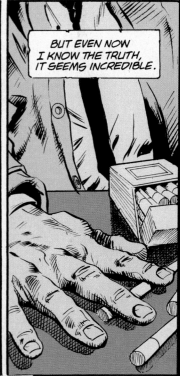
BUT EVEN NOW I KNOW THE TRUTH, IT SEEMS INCREDIBLE.

AH... MISTER CONSTANTINE. PLEASE COME IN.

HAVE A SEAT.

CHEERS, DOC. YOUR SECRETARY SAID YOU HAD THE RESULTS OF THE TESTS, YEAH?

I KNEW SOMETHING WAS WRONG THE MINUTE HE DIDN'T OFFER ME TEA. NO RELAXING CUPPA.. NO BULLSHIT. WHATEVER HE HAD TO SAY WAS TOO BIG FOR THAT.

UMMM... THE RESULTS. YES.

MISTER CONSTANTINE, I'D... I HAVE TO ASK...

I'M SORRY, MISTER CONSTANTINE. IT'S BAD NEWS.

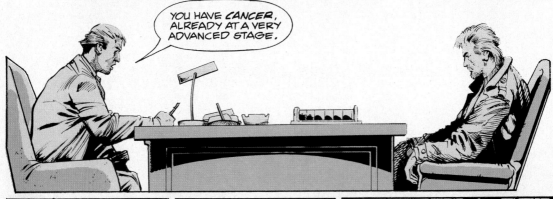

YOU HAVE CANCER, ALREADY AT A VERY ADVANCED STAGE.

IT'S YOUR LUNGS. I'M... I'VE DOUBLE CHECKED THE TESTS, AND I'M AFRAID...

IT'S TERMINAL.

I DIDN'T REALLY LISTEN TO THE REST OF IT.

HE TALKED FOR SOME TIME, ABOUT GROWTHS AND CELL DEATH AND WEAKENED LUNGS. SHOWED ME CHARTS I PRETENDED TO READ.

ASKED ME HOW MANY FAGS I WENT THROUGH A DAY.

TWENTY OR THIRTY, I TOLD HIM.

Ah, WELL THERE YOU ARE, HE SAID.

AND THAT WAS IT.

HE OFFERED TO MAKE ARRANGEMENTS TO HELP THE LAST FEW MONTHS GO BY A LITTLE EASIER, AND I SAID I'D THINK ABOUT IT.

I JUST WANTED TO GET OUT, TO BE HONEST. HE WAS SO OBVIOUSLY UNCOM-FORTABLE.

AS I LEFT THE WAITING ROOM, I HEARD HIM TELLING HIS SECRETARY TO CANCEL HIS APPOINTMENTS FOR THE REST OF THE AFTERNOON.

I'M PRETTY SURE THAT WAS MORE FOR MY BENEFIT THAN ANYTHING ELSE.

OUTSIDE, IN THE WARM SPRING BREEZE, IT BEGAN TO SINK IN.

THEY'D KILLED ME. NOT DEMONS, NOT MURDERED FETUS-TWINS,..., THEM...

THERE WAS A NEWSAGENT'S SOLD SILK CUT ROUND THE CORNER, THOUGH, SO THAT WAS OKAY.

ANYWAY, WHO WAS I TRYING TO KID?

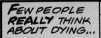

FEW PEOPLE **REALLY** THINK ABOUT DYING...

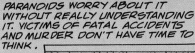

PARANOIDS WORRY ABOUT IT WITHOUT REALLY UNDERSTANDING IT. VICTIMS OF FATAL ACCIDENTS AND MURDER DON'T HAVE TIME TO THINK.

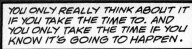

YOU ONLY REALLY THINK ABOUT IT IF YOU TAKE THE TIME TO. AND YOU ONLY TAKE THE TIME IF YOU KNOW IT'S GOING TO HAPPEN.

THAT'S WHEN THE THOUGHT OF DEATH TAKES UP YOUR EVERY WAKING MOMENT...

WHAT **ELSE** IS THERE TO DO?

I'M GOING TO **DIE**, THOUGH. THAT'S THE THING THAT GETS ME.

NO MORE LIFE. NO MORE STARING OUT ACROSS THE CITY, OR GETTING PISSED, OR STROLLING ROUND THE WORLD HUNTING DOWN THE MONSTERS.

OR SEEING MY FRIENDS...

MY FRIENDS ARE ALL BUTCHERED OR LOST OR SCATTERED, GONE A LONG TIME AGO.

STILL...

...THAT'S NEVER STOPPED THEM BEFORE.

LAST NIGHT, I DIDN'T SLEEP WELL AT ALL.

MAYBE I WAS BURIED ALIVE... MAYBE I JUST STAYED IN MY BODY...BUT I FELT AND HEARD AND SAW AND KNEW *EVERYTHING*.

THE SLIMY FLICKER OF THE EMBALMER'S HANDS, AND A TASTE OF THE FLUID ON THE COTTON WADS HE CRAMMED INTO MY CHEEKS.

THE BEGINNING OF A LONG DARKNESS WHEN THE LID WAS NAILED SHUT.

THE AWFUL LURCH WHEN THE COFFIN CAME TO REST, SIX FEET DOWN.

THE FIRST RATTLE OF SOIL AND PEBBLES ABOVE ME.

A SENSE OF PRESSURE ON THE LID...

THEN SILENCE... BLACKNESS... NOTHING.

I WASN'T EXPECTING WHAT HAPPENED NEXT.

JOHN.

NO...THAT'S NOT TRUE.

I WAS EXPECTING IT, ALL RIGHT.

JOHN.

BUT YOU ALWAYS *HOPE*.

JOHN.

uh...

I KNOW YOU, DON'T I?

COURSE. I'M *ASTRA* REMEMBER? FROM NEW-CASTLE?

BUT...YOU *DIED* BECAUSE OF ME, SWEETHEART! I GOT YOU *KILLED*--

YEAH, BUT YOU'RE DEAD TOO, AREN'T YOU?

NOW *YOU* KNOW WHAT IT'S LIKE!

WAIT A MINUTE, ASTRA--JUST HOLD IT, OKAY?

I DON'T THINK I *WANT* THIS...

I'M *SORRY*, JOHN, BUT WE ALL HAVE TO DO THIS, YOU KNOW.

YOUR FRIENDS DID.

OH, *SHIT!*

AND HELLO TO *YOU.*

YOU... I THOUGHT YOU'D LEAVE ME ALONE, NOW...

YOU GOT US ALL *BUMPED OFF,* YOU WANKER. WE'RE NOT GONNA FORGET *THAT* IN A HURRY.

GIVE US A BREAK! I WIPED OUT THE BASTARDS THAT DID FOR YOU--

FAT LOT OF GOOD *THAT* DID US, YOU CHEAP LITTLE SHIT.

WELL YOU CAN PISS **OFF,** YOU OLD FOSSIL! I'VE FINISHED OFF NERGAL AND I'VE KILLED THAT NUTTER WHO CUT YOU TO PIECES, AND YOU'RE SUPPOSED TO LEAVE ME **ALONE,** NOW!

YOU SODDING GHOSTS ARE MEANT TO BE AT **REST!**

WHH-WUH-WE'RE NOT GUHHH... NOT GUHHH... GUHHHHH--

THAT'S EASY FOR **YOU** TO SAY, ZITFACE. MIND YOU, I CAN SEE YOUR PROBLEM... VIRGIN AT TWENTY, RIGHT?

HERE'S ONE GHOST THAT'LL **NEVER** GET LAID!

UNLESS YOU COUNT THE DOG-**AAOOW!**

YOU'VE ALWAYS HAD A **VICIOUS STREAK,** HAVEN'T YOU? JUST LIKE THE TWISTED LITTLE BOY WHO NEARLY KILLED HIS OWN **FATHER.**

WELL, IF YOU'D LISTENED TO BENJAMIN INSTEAD OF LASHING OUT, YOU'D HAVE HEARD WHY WE'RE **HERE.**

I'LL RIP YOUR **FRIGGIN'** HEAD OFF, YOU MOTHERFU--

LEAVE HIM, FRANK.

OKAY. COME ON, THEN. LET'S HEAR IT.

WE'RE **NOT** GHOSTS ANY-MORE. WE'RE **NOT** HAUNT-ING YOU.

YOU CAN'T HAUNT THE DEAD.

THERE WAS BLOOD ALONG WITH THE PUKE, AND A BIT OF THE OTHER STUFF.

JUST SEEMED TO KEEP COMING UP. I PICTURED MYSELF STUCK THERE FOREVER...

...UNTIL I WAS JUST AN EMPTY SKIN AND A BOG FULL OF PUKE.

I SAT THERE 'TIL DAWN. HAVEN'T HAD ANY SLEEP SINCE.

THANK GOD.

JUST A DREAM. I THOUGHT I WAS OVER THE WORST OF THOSE, BUT...

IN THE OLD DAYS, THE GHOSTS AND THE DREAMS CAME TO ME. AND WHEN I DID WHAT THEY WANTED, THEY LEFT ME ALONE.

SO I WAS OVER ALL THAT. THIS WAS SOMETHING NEW, AND MY FRIENDS IN THE DREAM WERE RIGHT.

THEY'RE NOT GHOSTS ANYMORE. THEY'RE NOTHING MORE THAN MEMORIES.

AND YEAH, I WENT TO THEM.

BUT THAT WAS ALL JUST A DREAM. I CAN DEAL WITH THAT.

NO, THE REAL NIGHTMARE...

THAT BEGAN TODAY.

SO, WHAT BRINGS YOU TO THIS PART OF THE WORLD, JOHN?

THING IS, MARK, I'M LOOKING FOR A BIT OF A FAVOR--

A FAVOR? OHH, WHAT A SURPRISE!

I'M SORRY, MATE. I KNOW I OWE YOU A FEW AS IT IS, BUT...

MY AUNT DOLLY'S NOT TOO WELL. CANCER.

OH, GOD, JOHN... I DIDN'T REALIZE...

IT'S HER LUNGS, Y'SEE. SHE'S GOT TO GO INTO HOSPITAL SOON, AND I HATE TO SEE HER WASTING AWAY WITH NOBODY SHE KNOWS NEAR HER...

WELL, IF YOU LIKE, I CAN SHOW YOU ROUND THE CANCER WARD HERE, JOHN. GIVE YOU A ROUGH IDEA AT LEAST, MMM?

I WAS HOPING YOU WOULD, MATE. CHEERS.

HAS HER DOCTOR GIVEN HER MUCH OF A CHANCE?

'FRAID NOT. FEW MONTHS LEFT, HE RECKONS.

AHH, ROUGH BUSINESS.

THIS IS IT.

IF IT'S TERMINAL, ALL WE CAN DO, REALLY, IS PUMP THEM FULL OF DRUGS. NEVER QUITE *STOPS* THE PAIN, BUT... WELL, IT EASES IT A LITTLE.

THESE PATIENTS ARE ALL ON MEDICATION AT THE MOMENT.

YOU MEAN THEY'RE ALL GOING TO--

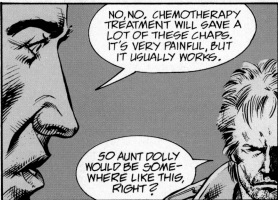

NO, NO. CHEMOTHERAPY TREATMENT WILL SAVE A LOT OF THESE CHAPS. IT'S VERY PAINFUL, BUT IT USUALLY WORKS.

SO AUNT DOLLY WOULD BE SOMEWHERE LIKE THIS, RIGHT?

mmm... BUGGER!

LOOK, I HAVE TO *GO*, JOHN. CAN YOU SEE YOUR-SELF OUT?

eh? OH, SURE.

CHEERS.

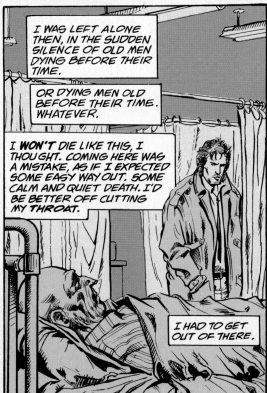

I WAS LEFT ALONE THEN, IN THE SUDDEN SILENCE OF OLD MEN DYING BEFORE THEIR TIME.

OR DYING MEN OLD BEFORE THEIR TIME. WHATEVER.

I *WON'T* DIE LIKE THIS, I THOUGHT. COMING HERE WAS A MISTAKE, AS IF I EXPECTED SOME EASY WAY OUT. SOME CALM AND QUIET DEATH. I'D BE BETTER OFF CUTTING MY *THROAT*.

I HAD TO GET OUT OF THERE.

OI! BLONDIE!

uh...WHAT CAN I DO FOR YOU, GRAMPS?

CHEEKY LITTLE BASTARD.

GOT A FAG?

WOULD'VE THOUGHT YOU'D BE OFF THEM, CHUM. SILK CUT OKAY?

NO CAMELS?

SHIT, I'M BEGINNING TO SEE WHY YOU'RE HERE...

HAHAHAHAHA! A SMART-ARSE, EH?

UH-HUH. JOHN'S THE NAME.

CHEERS, JOHN. I'M MATT. YOU VISITING SOMEONE?

FOR JUST A MOMENT I THOUGHT OF TELLING HIM THE AUNT DOLLY STORY, BUT I LIKED THIS OLD BLOKE.

NO LIES.

NAH. WAS THINKING OF MOVING IN MYSELF IN A WEEK OR TWO, MATT.

WE FELL EASILY INTO CONVERSATION AFTER THAT. I TOLD HIM ABOUT THE SPITTING AND YESTERDAY'S SHOCK DISCOVERY.

AS FOR HIM, HE'D BEEN WITH THE DESERT RATS AT ALAMEIN, COME HOME TO A LIFE THAT COULD NEVER QUITE EQUAL THE THRILL OF HIS ARMY DAYS, DRUNK AND SMOKED ENOUGH TO KILL HIM--AND ENDED UP HERE.

DYING IN A COUNTRY THAT HE DIDN'T KNOW ANYMORE, BECAUSE ALL THE MONEY WAS SPENT ON GETTING A WHORE INTO OFFICE EVERY FOUR YEARS.

SO, WHAT'RE YOU GOING TO DO, SON? I GET THE FEELING YOU'RE NOT LOOKING FORWARD TO LIFE IN THE SHITHOLE, HERE.

NURSES ARE NICE, MIND.

HEH. YOU'RE RIGHT, THOUGH. DON'T THINK I'LL BE MOVING IN WITH YOU.

YOU WOULDN'T *TOP* YOURSELF, I HOPE. MORTAL SIN, THAT.

ABOUT AS MORTAL AS YOU CAN GET... BUT NO, I DON'T THINK I'LL DO MYSELF IN, EITHER. TELL YOU THE TRUTH, I HAVEN'T GOT A BLOODY CLUE WHAT I'LL DO.

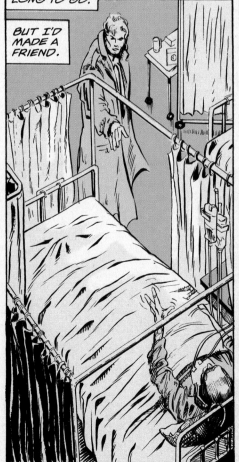

WE LEFT IT AT THAT, BUT I PROMISED I'D COME BACK AND VISIT. I DIDN'T SAY "SOON," BECAUSE THAT WAS OBVIOUS. NEITHER OF US HAD VERY LONG TO GO.

BUT I'D MADE A FRIEND.

OUTSIDE, I STILL DIDN'T KNOW WHAT TO DO. I FELT ANNOYED, AS IF MY INDECISION WAS WHAT WAS KILLING ME, AND NOT THE CANCER.

I'D KNOWN ALL ALONG THAT THERE WERE SEVERAL THINGS I *MIGHT* TRY TO GET ME OUT OF THIS.

I WAS ALSO SURE THAT NONE OF THEM WOULD ACTUALLY *WORK*, SO I'D NO REAL INCLINATION TO TRY THEM.

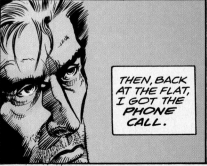

THEN, BACK AT THE FLAT, I GOT THE *PHONE CALL*.

YEAH?

MISTER CONSTANTINE? DOCTOR ELLIS HERE-- WE SPOKE YESTERDAY, REMEMBER?

YOU DON'T THINK I'M GONNA FORGET *THAT*, DO YOU?

HEHEH...UM, THE THING IS, MISTER CONSTANTINE, I'VE BEEN RE-VIEWING THE TEST RESULTS, AND

A SINGLE MAD MOMENT AS MY MIND SCREAMED AND BEGGED AND PLEADED FOR THE NEXT WORDS TO BE "YOU'RE NOT GOING TO DIE"--

I'VE TURNED UP SOMETHING RATHER *INTERESTING*.

UH... INTERESTING?

YES, IN YOUR *BLOOD* SAMPLE. IT'S THROWN UP SOME HIGHLY UNUSUAL ELEMENTS, YOU SEE.

TO BE HONEST, I WOULDN'T KNOW *HOW* TO CHARACTERIZE THEM...THEY'RE NOT ENZYMES, OR CELLS, OR ANYTHING I'VE COME ACROSS BEFORE--

I WAS WONDERING IF YOU COULD COME IN FOR SOME MORE TESTS, MISTER CONSTANTINE...

SHIT.

MISTER CONSTANTINE?

IT'S

DEMON BLOOD

ARSEHOLE!

HE WANTED THE *BLOOD*. OH, HE'D NEVER SEEN ANY-THING LIKE *THAT* BEFORE.

OH, NO.

I'VE BEEN HERE TWO HOURS, NOW. IT WAS **MEANT** TO BE A PLANNING SESSION, BUT...

...THE ANGER'S GONE, AND THE FEAR'S COME BACK.

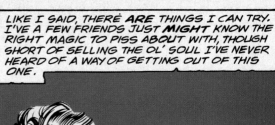

LIKE I SAID, THERE **ARE** THINGS I CAN TRY. I'VE A FEW FRIENDS JUST **MIGHT** KNOW THE RIGHT MAGIC TO PISS ABOUT WITH, THOUGH SHORT OF SELLING THE OL' SOUL I'VE NEVER HEARD OF A WAY OF GETTING OUT OF THIS ONE.

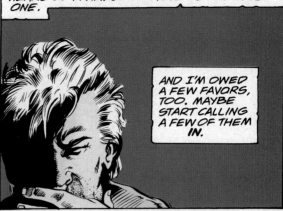

AND I'M OWED A FEW FAVORS, TOO. MAYBE START CALLING A FEW OF THEM **IN**.

THING IS--

RIGHT, SUNSHINE...

HUH?

YOU'VE GOT SOME BLOODY NERVE, MATE, SITTING HERE FOR **TWO HOURS** AND ONLY BUYING A CUP OF TEA!

YOU HAVEN'T EVEN **DRUNK** IT!

IT'S GONE **COLD**, HASN'T IT? YOU DON'T EXPECT ME TO DRINK COLD TEA, DO YOU?

WELL, IT'S **BOUND** TO GO COLD IF YOU LEAVE IT FOR TWO HOURS, ISN'T IT?

NO CHANCE OF A REFILL, THEN?

I MAY BE DYING OF CANCER, BUT I CAN STILL GET A LAUGH OUT OF BAITING MORONS.

THAT'S A GOOD SIGN.

NO IT'S NOT.

I'M *WELL* SCREWED HERE. THERE'S ALL THE STUFF I CAN TRY, AND I *WILL*. I'LL CLAW AND SCRATCH FOR ANY CHANCE OF LIFE, NO MATTER HOW REMOTE.

I DON'T EVEN KNOW IF I LIKE MY LIFE AT THE MOMENT, BUT I'M NOT SODDING LETTING GO OF IT UNTIL I FIND OUT.

BUT EVEN AS I TRY, EVEN AS I RUN THROUGH ALL THE OPTIONS, I KNOW DEEP DOWN IN MY HEART OF HEARTS...

...THAT I'LL FAIL.

THAT I'M GOING TO DIE.

CONTINUED IN THE TRADE PAPERBACK COLLECTION *DANGEROUS HABITS.*

THE HELLBLAZER LIBRARY

14 definitive collections chronicling the legendary anti-hero and his journeys through Hell and back. Where horror, dark magic and bad luck meet, John Constantine is never far away.

ORIGINAL SINS
JAMIE DELANO/VARIOUS
The volume that introduces John Constantine, master manipulator of black magic, and chronicles the inescapable nightmares that threaten his closest friends and loved ones.

DANGEROUS HABITS
GARTH ENNIS/VARIOUS
Constantine is diagnosed with terminal lung cancer and plays his most dangerous game ever in order to save his life while keeping his soul.

FEAR AND LOATHING
GARTH ENNIS/STEVE DILLON
Constantine must dissuade his young niece Gemma from following in his troubled footsteps, as well as engineer a fall from heaven and cope with an upcoming birthday.

TAINTED LOVE
GARTH ENNIS/STEVE DILLON
Constantine loses Kit, the love of his life, and spirals into homelessness and alcoholism. On the street he must deal with vicious vampires and revisit the scene of one of his earlier — and tragic — encounters with the black arts.

DAMNATION'S FLAME
GARTH ENNIS/STEVE DILLON/ WILLIAM SIMPSON/PETER SNEJBJERG
Cleaned up but still distraught, Constantine heads to New York City, where his body takes abuse on the streets as his mind is hijacked into a voodoo hell.

RAKE AT THE GATES OF HELL
GARTH ENNIS/STEVE DILLON
Looking for revenge after twice being tricked by him, the Devil confronts Constantine one final time in hopes of destroying him once and for all. Meanwhile, Constantine meets with Kit and hears her bittersweet homecoming story.

SON OF MAN
GARTH ENNIS/JOHN HIGGINS
Constantine must put right an old mistake that has left his best mate Chas Chandler wrongly accused of killing a mob boss and an undead child about to unleash unimaginable evil on the world.

HAUNTED
WARREN ELLIS/JOHN HIGGINS
Constantine looks into the death of an old love and earns a savage beating for his trouble. But when the killer makes the mistake of exposing his identity, the Hellblazer teaches him the real meaning of revenge.

SETTING SUN
WARREN ELLIS/VARIOUS
Five short stories follow Constantine as he deals with a room-bound psychotic, the "crib" of a miscarried Antichrist, the guilty conscience of a World War II torturer, a desperate conspiracy theorist and the ghosts of old loves.

HARD TIME
BRIAN AZZARELLO/RICHARD CORBEN
Convicted for a murder he didn't commit, Constantine is sentenced to 35 years in an American maximum security prison. However, using his wits and mastery of black magic, he soon climbs the ranks to become top dog of his new, horrible environment.

GOOD INTENTIONS
BRIAN AZZARELLO/MARCELO FRUSIN
In the small town of Doglick, West Virginia, Constantine must confront the brothers of the man he went to prison for killing. While there, he rediscovers the fact that not all horrors are supernatural.

FREEZES OVER
BRIAN AZZARELLO/MARCELO FRUSIN/
GUY DAVIS/STEVE DILLON
Held hostage by a blizzard, an urban legend known as the "Iceman" and three desperate gunmen, Constantine must gamble with his life in order to save a group of innocent hostages.

HIGHWATER
BRIAN AZZARELLO/VARIOUS
From a white supremacist stronghold in Idaho to an underground sex club in California, Constantine's trek across America comes to an end in the stately manor of a nemesis he barely even knew he had.

ALL HIS ENGINES
MIKE CAREY/LEONARDO MANCO
A mysterious plague puts millions into deadly comas, including Chas's granddaughter, Tricia. In looking for a cure, Constantine discovers a mad demon in a body woven out of cancer cells, and a diabolical plot to build franchised Hells throughout the cities of men.